Extractive and Azeotropic Distillation

Extractive and Azeotropic Distillation

Based on papers presented at

two symposia sponsored by the

Division of Industrial and

Engineering Chemistry

of the American Chemical Society

at the 160th Meeting, Chicago,

Ill., Sept. 17, 1970, and the

163rd Meeting, Boston, Mass.,

April 14, 1972.

Dimitrios P. Tassios

Symposia Chairman

ADVANCES IN CHEMISTRY SERIES **115**

AMERICAN CHEMICAL SOCIETY
WASHINGTON, D. C.   1972

ADCSAJ 115 1-176 (1972)

Library of Congress Catalog Card 72-92811

ISBN 8412-0157-9

FOREWORD

ADVANCES IN CHEMISTRY SERIES was founded in 1949 by the American Chemical Society as an outlet for symposia and collections of data in special areas of topical interest that could not be accommodated in the Society's journals. It provides a medium for symposia that would otherwise be fragmented, their papers distributed among several journals or not published at all. Papers are refereed critically according to ACS editorial standards and receive the careful attention and processing characteristic of ACS publications. Papers published in ADVANCES IN CHEMISTRY SERIES are original contributions not published elsewhere in whole or major part and include reports of research as well as reviews since symposia may embrace both types of presentation.

CONTENTS

PREFACE

Azeotropic and extractive distillations have been used through the years in the chemical industry to separate mixtures where the relative volatility of the key components is very close, or equal, to unity. Applications from the classical dehydration of alcohol with benzene (*1*) to more recent ones such as the propylene–propane separation (*2*) and aromatics recovery from hydrocarbon mixtures with N-methylpyrrolidone (*3*), indicate a continuous interest through the years in this area.

These separation modes have not been used as frequently as they should in industry, and the often used reasons of high investment and high operating costs are often weak when one does an in-depth study. The real reason lies with the time and money required to obtain a satisfactory design (*4*). Because of the high nonideality of the systems involved, solvent selection, description of the nonideality of the phases, and tray-to-tray calculations are rather difficult. Recent developments in this area, however, should greatly facilitate this task, especially for extractive distillation. Solvent selection for azeotropic distillation is based on rather qualitative criteria discussed by Berg (*5*), but for extractive distillation the qualitative approach of Prausnitz and Anderson (*6*) and the empirical correlations of Pierotti *et al.* (*7*), Weimer and Prausnitz (*8*), Helpinstill and Van Winkle (*9*), along with the technique using gas–liquid chromatography by Tassios (*10, 11*) give reliable, rapid methods for solvent selection. For example, four to five solvents can be screened in one day by using gas–liquid chromatography. Also use of salts as extractive agents (*12*) provides a new dimension in extractive distillation separations.

The development of equations that successfully predict multicomponent phase equilibrium data from binary data with remarkable accuracy for engineering purposes not only improves the accuracy of tray-to-tray calculations but also lessens the amount of experimentation required to establish the phase equilibrium data. Such equations are: the Wilson equation (*13*), the non-random two-liquid (NRTL) equation (*14*), and the local effective mole fractions (LEMF) equation (*15, 16*), a two-parameter version of the basically three-parameter NRTL equation. Larson and Tassios (*17*) showed that the Wilson and NRTL equations predict accurately ternary activity coefficients from binary data; Hankinson *et al.* (*18*) demonstrated that the Wilson equation predicts accurately multicomponent vapor compositions—up to five components—from binary data. The same study indicates that when limited binary data are available, the one parameter Tassios–Wilson equation (19) predicts multicomponent—up to five components—data with generally good accuracy. The Wilson equation can also be used successfully to correlate phase equilibrium data in the presence of salts (20). The NRTL and LEMF equations can also predict successfully ternary liquid–liquid equilibrium data from the binary data with the latter providing better results (21). Regarding vapor phase nonidealities, the empirical correlation of O'Connell and Prausnitz (22) provide fugacity coefficients of sufficient accuracy for engineering purposes. Design considerations of azeotropic distillation schemes are discussed by Robinson and Gilliland (23), Hoffman (24), and recently by Black et al. (25), who present a computer oriented approach.

For extractive distillation the presence of the second feed (solvent) presents some computational complications in maintaining stable convergence in the solution by computers of the appropriate system of equations—i.e., material and enthalpy balances and equilibrium relationship. The algorithms that can inherently cope with multiple feeds are matrix oriented, and the Newton–Ramphson procedure of solving these equations shows the maximum degree of stability (4). Several papers discuss computational approaches for extractive distillation calculations (Amudson and Pontinen (26), Naphthali (27), Roche (4), Bruno et al. (28), Black and Ditsler (29), and others).

In conclusion, recent developments in solvent selection, phase nonideality description, and tray-to-tray calculation schemes have greatly facilitated the design of extractive and azeotropic distillation schemes, and use of salts give new methods for extractive distillation separations. Finally, the work of Gerster (30), Black and Ditsler (29), and Black et al. (25) compare these two schemes.

Dimitrios P. Tassios

Newark College of Engineering
Newark, N. J. 07102
July, 1972

Literature Cited

1. Guinot, H., Clark, F. W., *Trans. Inst. Chem. Engr. (London)* (1938) **16**, 187.
2. Hasflund, E. R., *Chem. Eng. Progr.* (1969) **65**, 9.
3. Mueller, E., Hoehfeld, G., *World Petrol. Congr., 8th*, Moscow (June 1971).
4. Roche, Ed., *160th Natl. Meet. Amer. Chem. Soc.*, Chicago, 1970.
5. Berg, L., *Chem. Eng. Progr.* (1969) **65**, 9, 52.

6. Prausnitz, J. M., Anderson, R., *A.I.Ch.E. J.* (1961) **7**, 96.
7. Pierotti, G. I., Deal, C. H., Derr, E. L., *Ind. Eng. Chem.* (1955) **51**, 95.
8. Weimer, R. F., Prausnitz, J., *Petrol. Refiner* (1965) **44**, 9, 237.
9. Helpinstill, J. G., Van Winkle, M., *Ind. Eng. Chem. Process Des. Develop.* (1968) **7**, 213.
10. Tassios, D. P., *Hydrocarbon Process.* (1970) **49**, 7, 144.
11. Tassios, D. P., *Ind. Eng. Chem. Process Des. Develop.* (1972) **11**, 43.
12. Furter, W. F., Cook, R. A., *Int. J. Heat Mass Transfer* (1967) **10**, 23.
13. Wilson, G. M., *J. Amer. Chem. Soc.* (1964) **86**, 127.
14. Renon, H., Prausnitz, J. M., *A.I.Ch.E. J.* (1968) **14**, 135.
15. Marina, J., Dissertation, Newark College of Engineering, Newark, 1972b.
16. Marina, J., Tassios, D. P., *Ind. Eng. Chem. Process Des. Develop.*, in press.
17. Larson, C. D., Tassios, D. P., *Ind. Eng. Chem. Process Des. Develop.* (1972) **11**, 35.
18. Hankinson, R. W., Langfitt, B. D., Tassios, D. P., *Can. J. Chem. Eng.*, in press.
19. Tassios, D. P., *A.I.Ch.E. J.* (1971) **17**, 1367.
20. Taques, D., Furter, W. F., *Advan. Chem. Ser.* (1972) **115**, 159.
21. Marina, J., Tassios, D. P., *Ind. Eng. Chem. Process Des. Develop.*, submitted for publication.
22. O'Connell, J., Prausnitz, J. M., *Ind. Eng. Chem. Process Des. Develop.* (1967) **6**, 245.
23. Robinson, C. S., Gilliland, E. R., "Elements of Fractional Distillation," p. 312, McGraw–Hill, New York, 1950.
24. Hoffman, E. S., "Azeotropic and Extractive Distillation," Wiley, New York, 1964.
25. Black, C., Golding, R. A., Ditsler, D. E., ADVAN. CHEM. SER. (1972) **115**, 64.
26. Amudson, N. R., Pontinen, A. J., *Ind. Eng. Chem.* (1958) **50**, 730.
27. Naphthali, L. M., *56th A.I.Ch.E. Meet.*, San Francisco (May 1965).
28. Bruno, J. A., Yanosik, J. L., Tierney, J. W., ADVAN. CHEM. SER. (1972) **115**, 122.
29. Black, C., Ditsler, D. E., ADVAN. CHEM. SER. (1972) **115**, 1.
30. Gerster, J. A., *Chem. Eng. Progr.* (1969) **65**, 9, 43.

Dehydration of Aqueous Ethanol Mixtures by Extractive Distillation

C. BLACK and D. E. DITSLER

Shell Development Co., Emeryville, Calif. 94608

Although nonidealities in vapor and liquid phases complicate the separation of components from mixtures, a knowledge of these nonidealities can be applied to design an extractive distillation step. Ethylene glycol is added to an aqueous ethanol mixture to produce the overhead separation of ethanol from water. Methods published earlier by one of the authors are applied to calculate phase equilibria in a computer calculation of the separation. The extractive distillation results are tabulated, represented graphically, and discussed to illustrate extractive distillation as a method for dehydrating aqueous ethanol mixtures. The results are compared with corresponding results obtained by azeotropic distillation with n-pentane as entrainer. They show extractive distillation with ethylene glycol is more expensive than azeotropic distillation with n-pentane.

Separating components from mixtures is complicated by nonidealities in the liquid and vapor phases. Nevertheless, a knowledge of the factors contributing to the nonideality of the mixtures helps to produce a judicious design for the separation step. Sometimes components are added to the mixture to alter the nonideality by changing the molecular environment.

Extractive distillation is used because the components are distributed differently between contacting liquid and vapor phases in equilibrium when a high-boiling nonideal component is added to the mixture. The added component is introduced in the upper part of a distillation column above the feed and remains in appreciable concentration in the liquid on all of the lower trays. It is removed from the column with one of the components being separated as the bottoms product. Although a nonideal component is also introduced for azeotropic distillation, the added com-

Table I.   Constants for Calculating Imperfection-Pressure Coefficients[a]

	T_c, $°K$	P_c, $Atm.$	E′	m	X
Ethanol	516.3	63.1	0.089	4.75	75.9
Ethylene glycol	761.11	84.04	0.089	4.75	79.2
Water	647.00	218.0	0.026	4.75	24.7

[a] All δ_{ij} coefficients have been taken equal to zero.

ponent is, in that case, more easily volatilized from the mixture than one of the components being separated. Consequently it is removed overhead from the column.

In either case the relative distributions between the separable liquid and vapor phases are predicted from the pure component vapor pressures $P_i°$, liquid phase activity coefficients, γ_i's, and imperfection-pressure coefficients θ_i's. Using these three quantities, the relative distribution is expressed as

$$\alpha_{ij} = \frac{\gamma_i P_i° \theta_j°}{\gamma_j P_j° \theta_i°} \tag{1}$$

Extractive distillation has been extensively used for nearly three decades in laboratory, pilot plant, and commercial plant operations. Calculation or prediction of phase equilibria for such separations has often been discussed (1, 2, 3). Some have discussed the selection of solvents for extractive distillation (4, 5). Others have discussed its recent application to particular separations (6, 7, 8). A comparison of extractive distillation, as a separation method, with azeotropic distillation and with liquid–liquid extraction has recently been discussed briefly by Gerster (9).

The use of digital computers to carry out complete calculations in the design of separation processes has been the goal of many. To do this effectively, suitable methods for phase equilibria and tray-to-tray distillation calculations are required. Results calculated by the application of such methods to dehydrate aqueous ethanol mixtures using ethylene glycol as the extractive distillation solvent is discussed below. A brief review of the methods used for phase equilibria and enthalpies is followed by a discussion of the results from distillation calculations. These are compared for extractive distillation with corresponding results obtained by azeotropic distillation with n-pentane.

Phase Equilibria

The important quantities needed to represent the nonideal phase equilibria for extractive distillation are vapor pressures $P_i°$, liquid-phase activity coefficients γ_i and imperfection-pressure coefficients θ_i. The

Table II.   Constants for Vapor Pressure Equations[a]

	A	B	C
Ethanol	8.16280	1623.22	228.98
Ethylene glycol	7.71147	1816.34	178.603
Water	20.844[b]	2817.4[b]	4.04859[b]

[a] Antoine equations.
[b] $\log P = A - B/T - C \log T$; P, mm Hg, T, °K.

critical constants and other coefficients for calculating the imperfection-pressure coefficients (*1*) are given in Table I. Equations and coefficients for calculating vapor pressures are given in Table II. As binary vapor interactions have been neglected, the values for the δ_{ij} coefficients have all been taken equal to zero as shown in Table I.

The Modified van Laar equations (*1*) have been used to calculate the liquid phase activity coefficients. Coefficients at three temperatures are given in Table III. These are used by the computer to calculate activity coefficients at any composition and temperature in the distillation column.

Enthalpies for saturated liquids and vapors are given in Table IV for the pure components referred to zero for the liquids at 32°F. Vapor mixtures are calculated assuming zero heat of mixing. Liquid enthalpies for the mixtures are calculated to include the integral heat of mixing, given according to

$$H_x^m = \Sigma x_i (L_i)_x \tag{2}$$

where the differential heat of mixing $(L_i)_x$ is given as

$$(L_i)_x = 2.303 R (\Delta \log \gamma_i)_x / \Delta(1/T) \tag{3}$$

Table III.   Modified van Laar Coefficients for the System Ethanol–Ethylene Glycol–Water

Binary$_{ij}$	A_{ij}	A_{ji}	C_{ij}	$t, °C$
Ethanol–ethylene glycol	0.276000	0.259279	0.000000	75.0
Ethanol–water	0.728000	0.407000	0.000000	75.0
Ethylene glycol–water	0.001680	0.001000	0.000000	75.0
Ethanol–ethylene glycol	0.251000	0.23579	0.000000	87.8
Ethanol–water	0.74600	0.40080	0.000000	87.8
Ethylene glycol–water	0.00142	0.00081	0.000000	87.8
Ethanol–ethylene glycol	0.23000	0.21607	0.000000	100.0
Ethanol–water	0.76050	0.39250	0.000000	100.0
Ethylene glycol–water	0.00130	0.000714	0.000000	100.0

Table IV.   Enthalpies for Liquid and Vapor

	$t\,°F$	h *(liquid)* Btu/lb. mole	H *(vapor)* Btu/lb. mole
Ethanol	32	0.00	19800.0
	100	2506.1	20937.9
	200	6034.9	22573.3
	300	10365.3	23969.2
Ethylene glycol	100	3637.0	30724.0
	200	7535.0	32828.0
	300	11600.0	35193.0
	400	15889.0	37700.0
Water	100	1225.0	19916.0
	200	3027.0	20649.0
	300	4820.0	21290.0

Distillation Calculations

Calculations for the extractive distillation of aqueous ethanol mixtures containing 85.64% *m* ethanol have been carried out with the aid of a UNIVAC 1108 computer. The computer program calculates all phase equilibria and tray-to-tray material and heat balances for each component

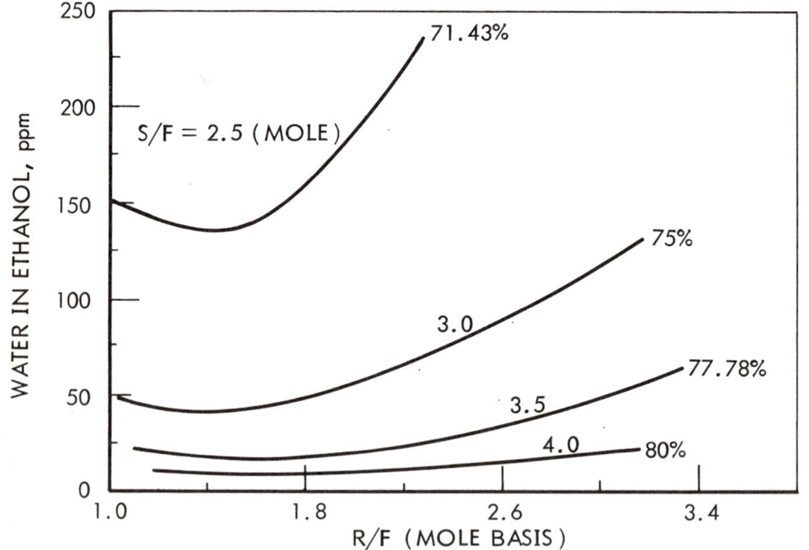

Figure 1.   *Effects on product purity of changing solvent–feed and reflux–feed ratios*

99% recovery of ethanol in the extractive distillation with ethylene glycol at 14.7 psia

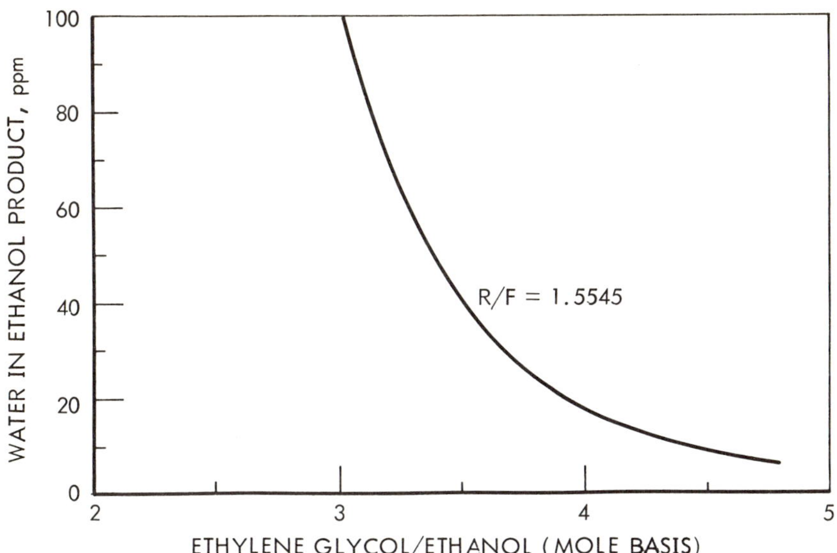

Figure 2.   *Effect of solvent–feed ratio on product purity in the extractive distillation of aqueous ethanol with ethylene glycol*

in the feed. For fixed ethylene–glycol feed ratios calculations were made for an ethanol recovery of 99% m in the overhead at four different reflux–feed ratios in the range 1–3⁺ mole basis. Each series of calculations was made at the constant solvent–feed ratios of 2.5, 3.0, 3.5, and 4.0 mole basis. The pressure drop per tray was assumed to be 0.1 psi with the reboiler pressure set at 14.7 psia. A drop of two psi from top tray to condenser was assumed for the calculation. The reflux temperature was set at 104.0°F. A total of 46 trays with solvent added on 43 and feed at tray 22 was used for the calculations. The feed and the solvent were introduced as liquid at 110° and 173°F, respectively.

These results have been used to show the effects of changing reflux–feed ratio at fixed values of the solvent–feed ratio. In Figure 1 the water in the ethanol product is plotted *vs.* the reflux–feed ratio, both expressed on a mole basis. Four curves are shown, each representing a different solvent–feed ratio. Each curve goes through a minimum as the reflux–feed ratio changes. At low solvent–feed ratios the minimum is more pronounced. At high solvent–feed ratios it is shallow, showing only small changes as the reflux–feed varies from 1.4–1.8, mole basis.

At the reflux–feed ratio of 1.5545 the water content of the top product, ethanol, is near the minimum for each solvent–feed ratio shown. For this reflux–feed ratio, the water content of the top product has been plotted *vs.* the ethylene glycol–ethanol ratios in Figure 2. This curve

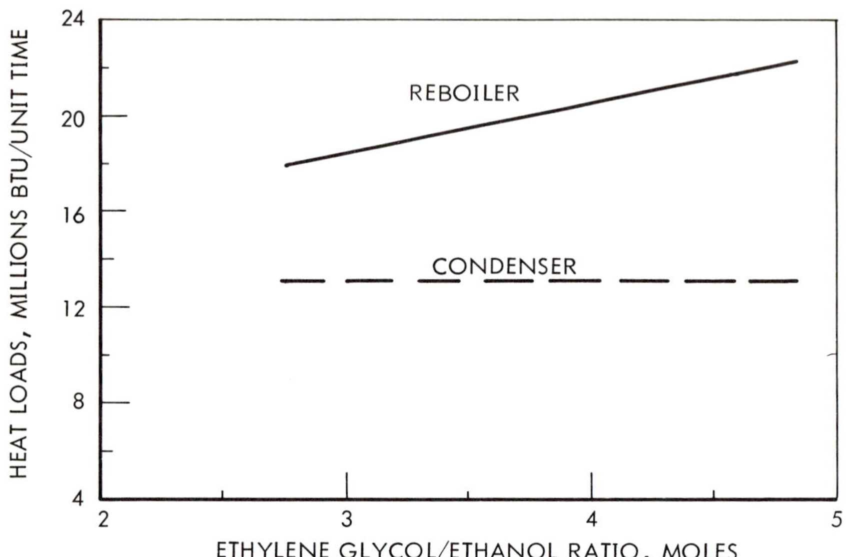

Figure 3.   Reboiler and condenser heat loads vs. solvent–feed ratio

99% recovery of ethanol, feed rate 242.02 moles ethanol/hour reflux/feed = 1.5545 mole basis

defines the water content of the ethanol product as a function of the solvent–ethanol ratio.

If the feed rate is fixed at 242.02 moles of ethanol per hour and the heat loads for reboiler and condenser are calculated, the effect of changing solvent–ethanol ratio can be obtained. These results are shown in Figure 3. Since ethanol is recovered at 99% mole in each case and the top

**Table V.   Extractive Distillation Column
Ethanol–Ethylene Glycol–Water at 14.7 Psia[a]**

Material Balance[b]

Components	Feed/Moles	Solvent/Moles	Top Product Moles	Bottom Product Moles
Ethanol	0.8564	—	0.856315	0.000085
Ethylene glycol	0.0000	3.5000	0.000001	3.499999
Water	0.1436	—	0.000014	0.143586
Totals	1.000	3.5000	0.856330	3.643670

[a] Reboiler load 73,969 Btu/unit time, top load 46,433 Btu/unit time.
[b] Liquid feed at 110°F on tray 22, liquid solvent at 173°F on tray 43.

Table VI. Extractive Distillation Column
Ethanol–Ethylene Glycol–Water

Temperature, Composition, and Volatility Profiles

Tray No.	t, °F	Ethanol in Vapor, Mole Fraction	Water in Liquid, Mole Fraction	P psia	α W/E
Condenser	104.0	0.999983	0.000016	8.20	—
46	156.9	0.999984	0.000015	10.20	1.11
44	158.7	0.999793	0.000013	10.4	1.09
43	195.3	0.987189	0.000011	10.5	0.485
42	195.8	0.987120	0.000019	10.6	0.486
40	196.6	0.98696	0.00005	10.8	0.488
38	197.5	0.98677	0.00011	11.0	0.489
36	198.4	0.98648	0.00024	11.2	0.490
34	199.2	0.98601	0.00051	11.4	0.492
32	200.0	0.98517	0.00107	11.6	0.493
30	200.9	0.98356	0.00220	11.8	0.493
28	201.7	0.98037	0.00454	12.0	0.492
26	202.7	0.97395	0.00934	12.2	0.489
24	203.7	0.96087	0.01926	12.4	0.482
22	194.8	0.93873	0.04539	12.6	0.532
20	195.5	0.93854	0.04546	12.8	0.533
18	196.3	0.93827	0.04561	13.0	0.534
16	197.0	0.93772	0.04600	13.2	0.535
14	197.7	0.93615	0.04731	13.4	0.535
12	198.5	0.93079	0.05201	13.6	0.532
10	199.5	0.91132	0.06951	13.8	0.516
8	202.0	0.83701	0.13805	14.0	0.452
6	218.5	0.53735	0.35352	14.2	0.274
4	246.2	0.07283	0.46407	14.4	0.208
2	297.9	0.00349	0.19499	14.6	0.311
1	362.1	0.00054	0.03941	14.6	0.428

product is always high purity ethanol, the top load for the condenser remains nearly constant. The reboiler load, however, reflects the change as the solvent–ethanol ratio varies.

Changing the recovery of ethanol from 99–99.99% m produces only minor increases in the heat loads. A summary of the column material balance for one mole of feed is shown in Table V when the solvent–feed ratio is 3.5 mole basis. This calculation was made for a recovery of 99.99% m ethanol using 46 equilibrium trays with the solvent on 43 and the feed on 22. The reflux–feed ratio was 1.5537 mole basis. The corresponding data for temperature, composition, and volatility profiles are summarized in Table VI.

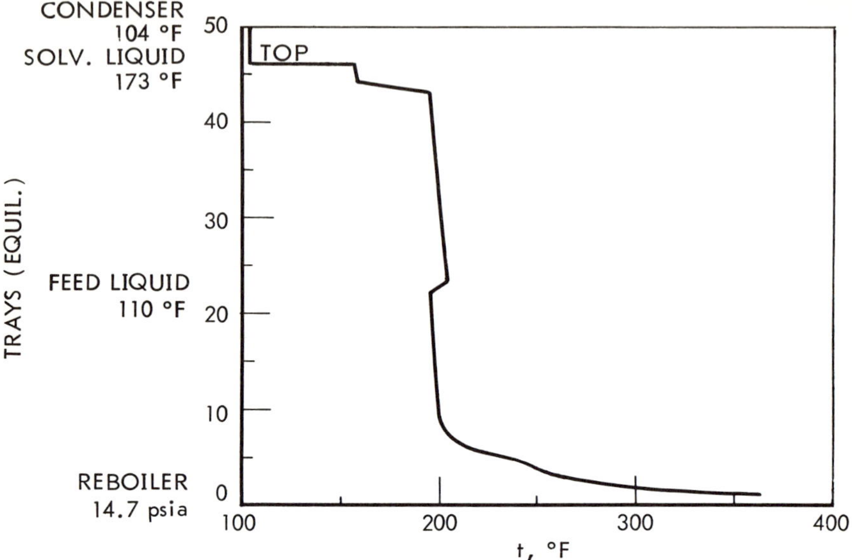

Figure 4.   *Temperature profile in extractive distillation of aqueous ethanol 99.99% recovery of ethanol, ethylene glycol/ethanol ratio = 4.08688 moles, reflux– feed 1.5537 moles*

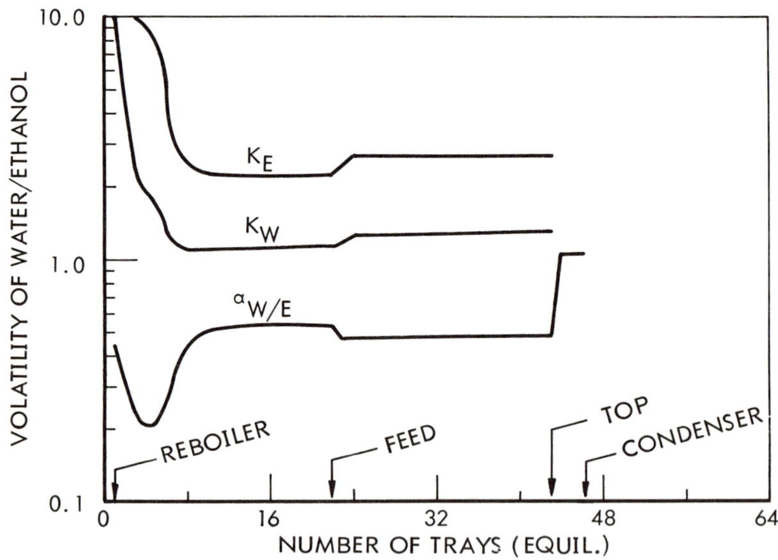

Figure 5.   *Volatility profiles in the extractive distillation of aqueous ethanol with ethylene glycol*

EG/E = 4.08688, R/F = 1.5537 moles, 99.99% recovery, ethanol

The temperature profile for the extractive distillation results of Table VI has been plotted in Figure 4. The high solvent input temperature and the low feed input temperature cause slightly higher temperatures in much more of the rectifying section than in the upper part of the stripping section. The corresponding volatility profile for the column is shown in Figure 5. The individual K values are also shown there. As the temperature increases upon approaching the reboiler, the relative volatility for water with respect to ethanol would decrease if the solvent concentration remained fixed. However the ethylene glycol concentration in the liquid increases, tending to make the relative volatility increase. These two opposing influences make the relative volatility curve go through a minimum near tray number four, as seen in Figure 5.

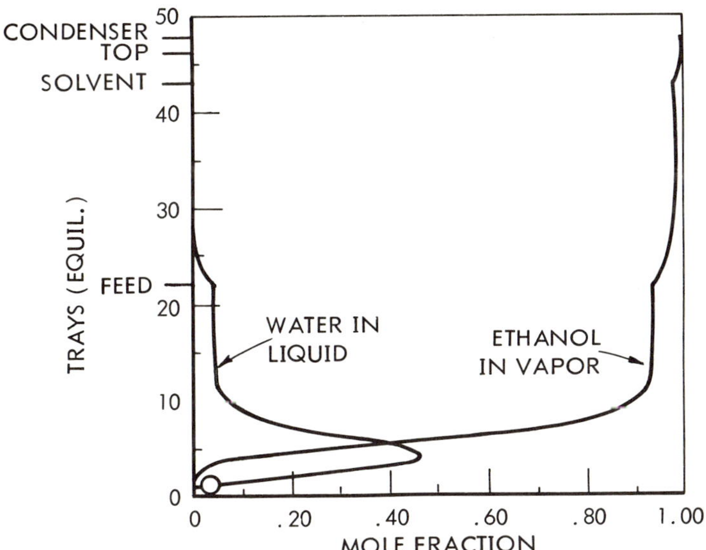

Figure 6.   Composition profiles in the extractive distillation of aqueous ethanol with ethylene glycol

EG/E = 4.08688 moles, R/F = 1.5537 moles, 99.99% recovery ethanol

Composition profiles for the same extractive distillation column are shown in Figure 6. The water concentration in the liquid goes through a pronounced maximum at about tray number four (*see* Table VI), corresponding to the minimum in the relative volatility of water with respect to ethanol. In this region the ethanol concentration in the vapor increases rapidly, changing from less than 2% at tray number three to more than 50% at tray number six. This rapid increase continues to about tray number ten where the concentration of ethanol in the vapor is about

$91\%\,m.$ Water drops out of the vapor in the rectifying section between the feed tray and the solvent input tray while ethanol continues to concentrate.

Above the solvent inlet the ethylene glycol drops out rapidly, so in three equilibrium trays it is reduced from about $1.3\%\,m$ to less than 2 ppm. The water content of the top product, ethanol, is about 16 ppm on a mole basis, as calculated from the results of Table V.

The bottom product from the extractive distillation column is aqueous ethylene glycol with $3.94\%\,m$ water. This is fed to a solvent recovery column where water is stripped from the ethylene glycol which is then recycled as solvent to the extractive distillation column.

Calculated results for the solvent recovery column with nine total trays having the feed inlet on tray five are given in Table VII. The reboiler pressure has been taken as 14.7 psia. The pressure drop per tray has been set at 0.09 psi. A drop of 1.7 psi from the top tray to the con-

Table VII. Solvent Recovery Column
Ethanol–Ethylene Glycol–Water

Temperature and Composition Profiles

Tray No.	$t, °F$	Water in Vapor, Mole Fraction	Ethylene Glycol in Liquid, Mole Fraction	P psia	α EG/W
10 Cond.	104.0	0.99936	.00004	12.28	—
9 Top	209.5	0.99936	.00176	13.98	.0216
8	213.3	0.99830	.06686	14.07	.0224
7	264.6	0.93928	.64743	14.16	.0352
6	356.8	0.42680	.95536	14.25	.0627
5 Feed	379.6	0.15285	.98755	14.34	.0699
4	387.6	0.04343	.99763	14.43	.0723
3	390.2	0.01103	.99919	14.52	.0731
2	391.1	0.00265	.99981	14.61	.0734
1 Reboiler	391.7	0.00056	.99996	14.70	.0736

Material Balance

Components	Feed Moles[a]	Top Product Moles	Bottom Product Moles
Ethanol	0.000085	.000085	.000000
Ethylene glycol	3.499999	.000006	3.499993
Water	0.143586	.143442	0.000144
Totals	3.643670	.143533	3.500137

Reboiler load 3,3015 Btu/Unit Time
Top load   2,8709 Btu/Unit Time

[a] Based on one mole of feed to the extractive distillation column which precedes the solvent recovery column.

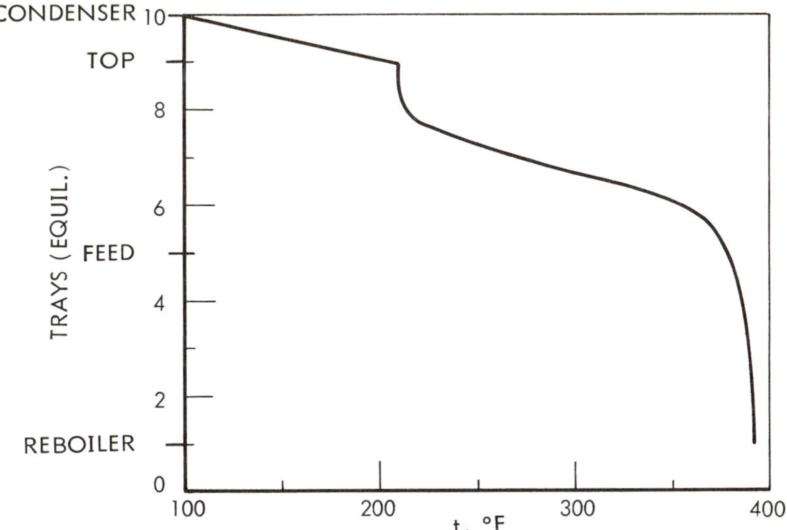

Figure 7.   Temperature profile for solvent recovery column

Stripping water from aqueous ethylene glycol

denser has been assumed. The reflux temperature was set at 104°F and
the reflux–feed ratio at 1.33491, mole basis. The feed temperature was
358°F, a few degrees less than the bottom temperature of the extractive
distillation column. Material balance and column profiles are given in
Table VII for the recovery column.

The temperature profile for this column is shown in Figure 7. The
composition profiles are plotted in Figure 8. These show the expected
trends, water in the vapor increasing and ethylene glycol in the liquid
decreasing as one proceeds from the reboiler to the top of the column.
With the number of trays shown and the reflux–feed ratio given, ethylene
glycol in the top product (water) is reduced to about 42 ppm, mole basis.
Ethanol in the water product is about 0.06% m.

Reducing ethylene glycol in the water product to a significantly lower
value requires only the addition of one or more rectifying trays in the
recovery column. An increase in the reflux–feed ratio will do as an
alternate method, but to change the ethanol in the water product, the
extractive distillation column would have to be operated for higher or
lower ethanol recovery than the 99.99% m value. This can be done without difficulty.

The bottom product from the solvent recovery column is ethylene
glycol with about 41 ppm of water, mole basis. By changing the number
of stripping trays in the solvent recovery column, this water content can
readily be decreased or increased.

If the top product (water) from the solvent recovery column is to be discarded, the two distillation columns would be operated to reduce ethanol and ethylene glycol to low concentrations, as illustrated in the calculations shown here. However, where the overall plant scheme is such that the water product might be recycled and used—e.g., as solvent to an aqueous extractive distillation, it might under some conditions be more economical to leave more ethanol in the water product. The ethanol would be recovered in the series of separation steps which follow in the flow scheme. Water might be rejected at a more suitable point in the flow scheme than from the top of the solvent recovery column. The best operating conditions can be determined only when the entire plant flow scheme is known.

Comparison of Extractive with Azeotropic Distillation

Although ethanol is obtained as a top product from an extractive distillation with ethylene glycol, it is obtained as a bottom product from an azeotropic distillation column using an entrainer such as *n*-pentane. Based on an ethanol rate of 242.02 moles per hour, a rough comparison will be made of the two separation methods.

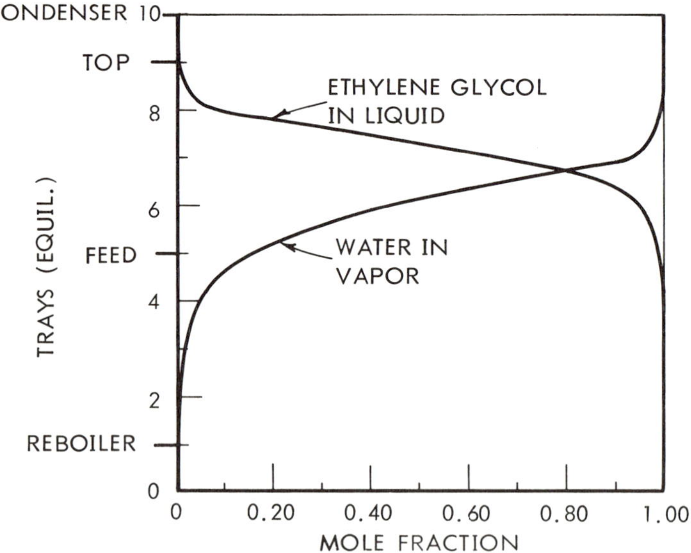

Figure 8.   Composition profiles for solvent recovery column
Stripping water from aqueous ethylene glycol

Table VIII.   Comparing Extractive and Azeotropic Distillation

Feed: Aqueous Ethanol (85.64%m Ethanol)

Extractive Distillation, 14.7 psia	*Azeotropic Distillation, 50 psia*
Solvent = ethylene glycol	Entrainer = n-pentane
Moles solvent–ethanol = 4.08688	Moles n-pentane–ethanol = 3.214
Reflux–feed ratio = 1.55369	
46 Trays total in extractive dist. col.	18 Trays total in azeotropic dist. col.
Solvent on tray 43	Entrainer on tray 18
Feed on tray 22	Feed on tray 16
Reboiler load = 20.9 million	Reboiler load = 10.7 million
Btu/hour[a]	Btu/hour[a]
Top load = 13.12 million	Condenser load = 11.33 million
Btu/hour	Btu/hour
Tower diameter = 5.3 feet	Tower diameter < 5 feet
Ethanol product:	Ethanol product:
Water 16 ppm (mole basis)	Water <3 ppm (mole basis)
Solvent 1.2 ppm (mole basis)	n-Pentane <1 ppm (mole basis)
Ethanol recovery from feed =	Ethanol recovery from feed
99.99%	>99.99%
Solvent recovery column	Stripping column
9 Trays, R/F = 1.33491 (mole)	
Reflux on tray 9	
Feed on tray 5	
Reboiler load = 9.33 million	Reboiler load <2. million
Btu/hour[a]	Btu/hour[a]
Top load = 8.11 million	Top load <2. million Btu/hour
Btu/hour	
Tower diameter = 4.1 feet	Tower diameter <2. feet
Total heat to reboilers = 30.23	Total heat to reboilers <13 million
million Btu/hour	Btu/hour
Total top loads = 21.23 million	Total top loads <14 million
Btu/hour	Btu/hour

[a] Based on 242.02 moles/hour of ethanol in feed to plant.

For the extractive distillation results of Tables V and VI, the reboiler load for the above ethanol rate would be about 20.9 million Btu per hour. The ethanol product contains about 16 ppm of water and about 1.2 ppm of ethylene glycol. For an ethanol recovery of 99.99%m, 46 total equilibrium trays are required with a reflux–feed ratio of 1.55⁺ and a solvent–ethanol ratio of 4.09⁻ mole basis. The condenser load is about 13.1 million Btu/hour, and the tower diameter is about 5.3 feet, based on a Glitsch sizing technique.

If n-pentane is selected as the entrainer for an azeotropic distillation scheme, an ethanol product containing less water than that obtained in the extractive distillation method is easily obtained with entrainer–ethanol ratios of 2.5–3.5, mole basis (*10*). For a ratio of 3.214, the water content of the ethanol is less than 3 ppm. Only 18 equilibrium trays are required in a column of less than 5 feet diameter. The heat loads in millions Btu/hour are about 10.7 for the reboiler and 11.3 for the condenser. A stripper is used to recover n-pentane and ethanol from the aqueous phase. The recovered n-pentane and ethanol can be recycled either to the feed or to the reflux stream of the azeotropic distillation column.

The stripper required to process the aqueous phase for recovering n-pentane and ethanol requires a few more trays, but it has a column diameter less than half that of the solvent recovery column for the extractive distillation scheme. The heat loads are also much smaller. The top product, consisting of n-pentane, ethanol, and some water, is recycled to the reflux stream of the extractive distillation column.

The results of calculations for the two separation methods are summarized in Table VIII. Fewer trays are required in the azeotropic distillation column than the extractive distillation column. The heat loads are also smaller. The quality of the ethanol product is also slightly better for the azeotropic distillation method. Including the stripper for processing the aqueous phase, the total heat load for reboilers for the azeotropic distillation method is less than half that for the extractive distillation method. The total condenser load is roughly two-thirds that for the extractive distillation method.

Although the azeotropic distillation scheme, using n-pentane, operates at a higher pressure, comparative calculations indicate this to be better than the extractive distillation scheme using diethylene glycol to dehydrate aqueous ethanol.

List of Symbols

H_x^M	the integral heat of mixing for mixture of composition x
$(L_i)_x$	the differential heat of mixing for component i at composition x
P_i°	vapor pressure for component i
P_j°	vapor pressure for component j
α_{ij}	volatility of component i relative to component j
γ_i	liquid phase activity coefficient for component i
γ_j	liquid phase activity coefficient for component j
θ_i	imperfection-pressure coefficient for component i
θ_j	imperfection-pressure coefficient for component j

Literature Cited

1. Black, C., Derr, E. L., Papadopoulos, M. N., *Ind. Eng. Chem.* (1963) **55,** No. 9, 38–47.
2. Garner, F. H., Ellis, S. R. M., *Trans. Inst. Chem. Eng. (London)* (1951) **29,** 45.
3. Null, H. R., Palmer, D. A., *Chem. Eng. Progr.* (1969) **65** (9), 47.
4. Berg, L., Chem. Eng. Progr. (1969) **65,** (9), 53.
5. Tassios, Dimitrios, *Chem. Eng.* (Feb. 10, 1969) **76** (3), 118–22.
6. Bannister, R. R., Buck, E., *Chem. Eng. Progr.* (1969) **65** (9), 65.
7. Halflund, E. R., *Chem. Eng. Progr.* (1969) **65,** 9.
8. Hoffman, E. S., "Azeotropic and Extractive Distillation," Wiley, New York, 1964.
9. Gerster, J. A., *Chem. Eng. Progr.* (1969) **65** (9), 43.
10. Black, C., Golding, R. A., Ditsler, D. E., *Advan. Chem. Ser.* (1972) **115,** 64.

RECEIVED November 24, 1970.

2

Process Design Considerations for Extractive Distillation: Separation of Propylene–Propane

ROMESH KUMAR, JOHN M. PRAUSNITZ, and C. JUDSON KING

Department of Chemical Engineering, University of California, Berkeley, Calif. 94720

Extractive distillation is evaluated as an alternative to ordinary distillation for the separation of propylene–propane mixtures. Particular attention is given to the necessary compromises between different design factors: solvent concentration within the primary column, solvent selectivity, solvent loss, etc. A major expense is associated with the sensible heat requirements of the circulating solvent; process modifications so as to minimize this expense are discussed. The process analysis explores combinations of solvent selectivity and other solvent properties which might make extractive distillation attractive. It appears that in almost all cases extractive distillation offers no advantage compared with ordinary distillation. Only in special cases may circumstances warrant extractive distillation. External factors favoring the use of extractive distillation are identified.

This work explores the important variables which must be considered to design an extractive distillation process. The discussion identifies the economic effects of these variables and their possible interactions. Some of the design variables may have synergistic effects in terms of separation cost while others may not. As a result, the optimum design for an economic extractive distillation process must be a compromise set of values for the different process variables. These compromises are discussed and are illustrated for a particular case—*i.e.,* separation of propane–propylene mixtures. For this commercially important separation fractional distillation is most often used, regardless of the low relative volatility (about 1.13–1.19 at 200 psia).

Extractive distillation is sometimes used to separate mixtures for which fractional distillation is difficult, such as for binary systems of close-boiling components or for multicomponent systems where the order of component volatilities does not correspond to the desired distribution of components between products. In extractive distillation, a separating agent, often called the solvent, is added to the mixture to be separated. This agent, or solvent, modifies the volatility of each component, one different from the other, by its effects on liquid-phase properties. Such effects can include forming association complexes, altering existing association structures, etc. As a result, the component relative volatilities in the presence of the solvent differ from those in the solvent-free mixture.

The fundamental flow diagram for an extractive distillation process is shown in Figure 1. The feed enters the extractive distillation column (primary column) in which the solvent is added near the top. The component (or components) whose volatility is the greatest in the presence of the solvent is driven overhead in this column. The bottoms consist of the solvent and the other component (or components); these are fed to the solvent recovery column (secondary column). The regenerated solvent is cooled and fed back to the primary column.

In most cases, the solvent is much less volatile than the feed components; it is therefore present mainly in the liquid phase in the primary column. This is desirable, as it is the liquid-phase nonidealities which give rise to the greater separation factor between the feed components. However, there is a relatively small amount of solvent in the vapor phase, and to avoid excessive loss of this solvent with the top product in the primary column, sufficient trays are provided above the solvent addition plate to reduce the solvent concentration in the top product to an acceptable level.

General Considerations

For the process shown in Figure 1, the main units are the two distillation columns (with their reboilers and overhead condensers) and the solvent cooler. The major utilities are the heat required in the reboilers and the cooling duties of the condensers and the solvent cooler. The design of the primary column depends primarily on the relative volatility of the key components; it is therefore strongly dependent upon the activity coefficients of these components in the solvent.

The volatilities of the feed components relative to the solvent are generally high; therefore, the design of the secondary column is primarily a function of the solvent circulation rate. The condenser duties depend on the reflux ratios in the two columns which are thus affected by the relative volatilities. The solvent cooler duty is a function of the solvent circulation rate and the recovery column reboiler temperature which is determined by the solvent volatility. The sum of the reboiler duties in

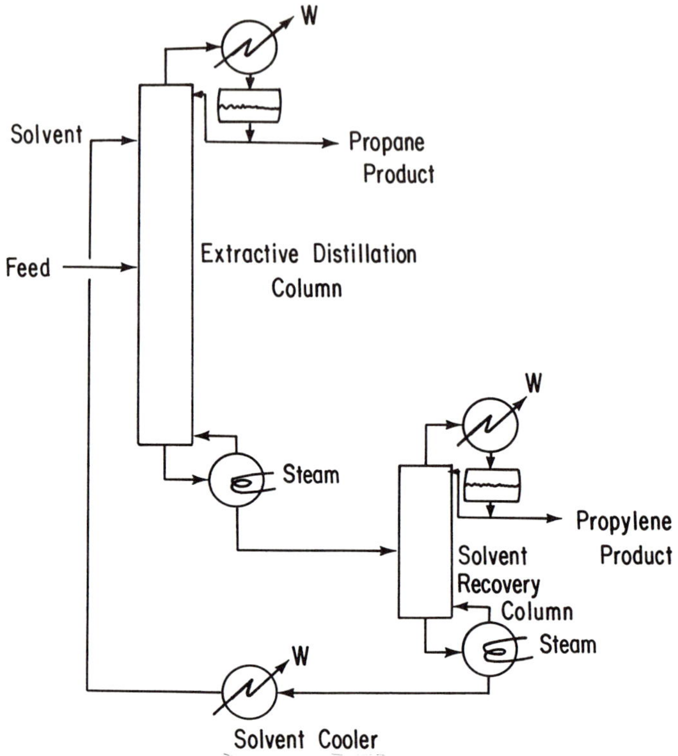

Figure 1.   Extractive distillation process flowsheet

the two columns is approximately equal to the sum of the heat removed in the condensers and in the solvent cooler. The thermodynamic properties of the solvent and the solvent recirculation rate are of major importance in the design of the extractive distillation process.

Solvent Selection Criteria

Important solvent characteristics are selectivity, miscibility with the feed, and volatility.

Selectivity. The selectivity, S^∞, is defined as the ratio of the activity coefficients of the key components when each alone is present in the solvent at infinite dilution. Thus, for the propane–propylene system

$$S^\infty = \gamma^\infty_{C_3H_8} / \gamma^\infty_{C_3H_6} \tag{1}$$

The activity coefficients of the components at other than trace concentrations in the solvent depend on the mixture composition and, for systems with positive deviation from Raoult's Law, decrease toward unity as the component mole fraction tends toward one. In a simple, symmetric binary system, the logarithm of the activity coefficient of the hydrocarbon (A) or (B) is proportional to the square of the solvent mole fraction (1)

$$\ln \gamma_A = (\ln \gamma^\infty_A) x_S^2$$
$$\ln \gamma_B = (\ln \gamma^\infty_B) x_S^2$$

$$(2)$$

Equation 2, although not highly accurate for many practical systems, was used in this work as it is convenient to implement and generally provides a good first-order approximation.

Neglecting vapor-phase corrections and the Poynting effect, the relative volatility between the key components in the presence of the solvent is

$$\alpha_{AB} = \frac{(\gamma_A)(P^\circ_A)}{(\gamma_B)(P^\circ_B)}$$

$$(3)$$

where P° is the pure-component saturation (vapor) pressure. Equation 3 may be written as

$$\alpha_{AB} = S\left(\frac{P^\circ_A}{P^\circ_B}\right)$$

$$(4)$$

where $S = \gamma_A/\gamma_B$

$$= S^\infty \cdot f(x_S)$$

such that $f(x_S) \to 1$ when $x_S \to 1$
    and $f(x_S) < 1$ for $x_S < 1$

A high selectivity gives a high relative volatility, making an easier separation possible. S increases with increasing solvent concentration (2), becoming a maximum at 100% solvent, and usually falls with rising temperature. An example is given in Figure 2, which shows the selectivity of the solvents furfural and acetonitrile for propane–propylene, as estimated by the procedures of Weimer and Prausnitz (3). S is largest at high solvent concentrations and at low temperatures; therefore, the separation would be easiest under these conditions.

The search for a suitable solvent for a particular separation would be greatly aided if the feed component activity coefficients could be predicted from the pure-component properties alone. Tassios (2) describes a five-step procedure for evaluating solvents for extractive distillation of hydrocarbons. Two of the more useful correlations for predicting activity coefficients are those proposed by Weimer and Prausnitz (3) and by Pierotti, Deal, and Derr (4). The former is useful where the feed components are saturated hydrocarbons, olefins, or aromatics. For other classes of hydrocarbons, the latter is useful.

For a paraffin–olefin system of the same number of carbon atoms in the absence of a solvent, the olefin is more volatile and is driven overhead

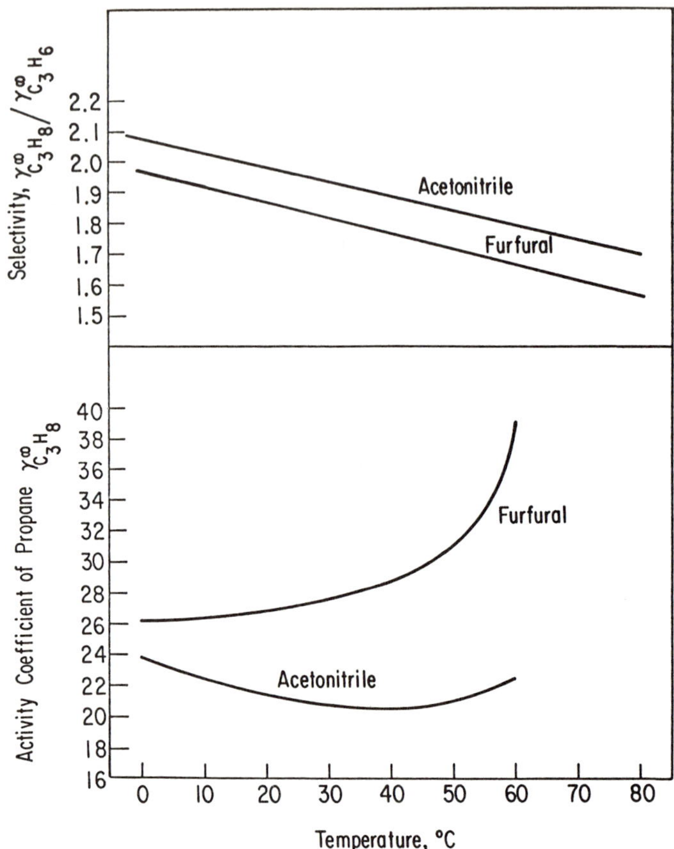

Figure 2. Effect of temperature on solvent selectivity and propane activity coefficient in furfural and in acetonitrile (calculated)

in ordinary distillation; for propane–propylene, $P^{\circ}_{C_3H_6}/P^{\circ}_{C_3H_8}$ is greater than unity. A polar solvent is used in extractive distillation of paraffin–olefin mixtures since the olefin, because of the large polarizability of the double bond, forms a less nonideal system with the solvent than does the paraffin. In these systems the paraffin activity coefficient is greater than that of the olefin, thereby tending to reverse the natural relative volatility of the paraffin–olefin system; for propane–propylene, $\gamma_{C_3H_6}/\gamma_{C_3H_8}$ is less than unity. To be useful, a solvent must reverse the relative volatility to such an extent that (α_{AB}) with solvent $> \left(\dfrac{1}{\alpha_{AB}}\right)$ without solvent.

Only a few experimental investigations have been reported which evaluate solvents for paraffin–olefin separations. Perhaps the most comprehensive experimental data on paraffin–olefin–solvent mixtures have been reported by Gerster, Gorton, and Eklund (*5*). These authors report activity coefficient data for *n*-pentane and 1-pentene in binary systems with 33 different solvents at four temperatures. The data for non-hydrogen bonding solvents were correlated in a plot of selectivity *vs.* ln $\gamma^{\infty}_{C_5H_{12}}$, as shown in Figure 3. The curve for hydrogen bonding solvents falls lower; *i.e.*, the same $\gamma^{\infty}_{C_5H_{12}}$ corresponds to a lower selectivity. Figure 3 shows that for a pair of hydrocarbon solutes containing the same number of carbon atoms, the activity coefficient of one hydrocarbon in binary solution with a polar solvent is, to a first approximation, a function of the activity coefficient of the other in that solvent. Activity coefficients for propane–propylene, as estimated by the method of Weimer and Prausnitz (*3*), exhibit behavior similar to that noted for activity coefficients of the *n*-pentane–1-pentene system within the accuracy of the estimation procedure.

However, Hafslund (*6*) has quoted solvent selectivity data for the propane–propylene system which deviate considerably from the plot given in Figure 3. Some of these data are also shown in that figure. It appears that although most solvents may be expected to fall along the

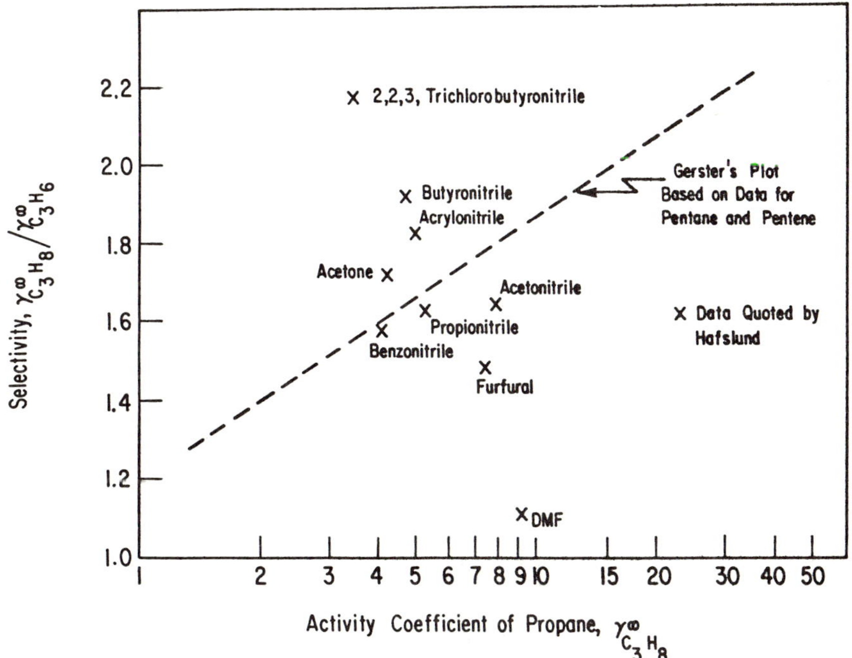

Figure 3.   Solvent selectivity as a function of activity coefficient of paraffin in the solvent

plot in Figure 3, there are some solvents which show substantially different selectivity. In this work, two sets of calculations were made for the effect of selectivity on the process design:

(1) $\gamma^{\infty}_{C_3H_8}$ varied with S^{∞} according to the plot in Figure 3.
(2) $\gamma^{\infty}_{C_3H_8}$ was held constant with varying values of S^{∞}.

Miscibility with the Feed Components. In a solute–solvent system exhibiting strong positive deviations from Raoult's Law, the solute has only limited solubility in the solvent. Above a certain solute concentration, two liquid phases are formed. The presence of two liquid phases on the plates of a distillation column leads to instability and operational problems. It is therefore necessary to ensure that the solute concentration in the liquid phase never exceeds its solubility limit. This solubility limit gives a minimum feasible solvent concentration in the section below the solvent addition plate of the primary column.

An approximation to the miscibility limit in a binary system is obtained by assuming that the polar solvent is essentially insoluble in the hydrocarbon. Since the activity of the hydrocarbon in the hydrocarbon phase is near unity, at equilibrium it must be the same as that in the solvent-rich phase.

$$\gamma_A x_{A_m} \approx 1 \tag{5}$$

If we further assume that Equation 2 holds for the binary system, we have

$$0 = (\ln \gamma^{\infty}_A)(1 - x_{A_m})^2 + \ln x_{A_m} \tag{6}$$

Knowing $\ln \gamma^{\infty}_A$, Equation 6 yields x_{A_m}, the mole fraction of A at the limit of its miscibility in the solvent.

Volatility. For a fixed tower pressure, the volatility of the solvent determines the reboiler temperature. It also influences the number of equilibrium stages required in the solvent-recovery column, as well as the number of stages required in the solvent knock-out section of the primary column. For process economics, the more important of these factors is generally the temperature of the bottoms from the solvent-recovery column since this is the highest solvent temperature in the process. The lowest solvent temperature is where the solvent is fed into the primary column. The change in solvent temperature is produced by the solvent cooler, and the greater the temperature swing between the hottest and the coolest points in the solvent circuit, the higher is the heat-transfer duty of the solvent cooler.

The sum of the heat duties in the reboilers is approximately equal to the sum of the heat duties of the overhead condensers and the solvent cooler. Since the solvent volatility influences the temperature level in the reboilers, it affects the heat input to the reboilers as well as the heat duty of the solvent cooler.

A secondary effect of the solvent volatility is on the operating temperature of the extractive distillation column. A more volatile solvent results in a lower average plate temperature. At the lower temperature, the separation factor is generally higher because of higher selectivity.

Table I.   Design Basis

Feed	Rate =	415 lb moles/hr
	Composition =	50 mole % C_3H_8, 50 mole % C_3H_6
	Condition =	saturated vapor at the tower pressure[a]
Propylene	Purity =	99.0%
	Recovery =	95.0%
	Capacity =	75 million lbs/yr
Solvent	Amount in each hydro-carbon product =	$\leqslant$0.01 mole %
	Normal boiling point =	140°F
	Other physical properties =	those of acetone
	Concentration at solvent feed plate =	0.85 to 0.90 mole fraction
	S^∞ =	1.7 to 3.1
	$\gamma^\infty_{C_3H_8}$ =	6.0 to 16.0
Coolant	Coolant =	water
	Inlet temperature =	70°F
	Temperature rise in condensers =	20°F
	Minimum approach temperature =	10°F
Cooler/Process Heat Exchangers	Minimum approach temperature =	20°F

[a]For binary distillation without solvent, the feed condition was taken as saturated liquid at the tower pressure.

Process Design

Process calculations were made for the separation of a propane–propylene mixture with the design basis shown in Table I. For the present calculations, the solvent physical properties were taken as those of acetone. The solvent selectivity and the hydrocarbon activity coefficients were varied over the ranges given in Table I. A stage-to-stage (Lewis–Matheson) method (7) was used to calculate the number of equilibrium stages required in the two towers, allowing for variations in α_{AB} and interstage molar flows from stage to stage. The stage-to-stage, material- and en-thalpy-balance procedure was also used for the fractional distillation alter-native, using the vapor–liquid equilibrium data of Reamer and Sage (8) for the propane–propylene binary system.

The basis and various parameters for the economic analysis are given in Table II. The overall column efficiency used was obtained from a plot of efficiency *vs.* the product of relative volatility and liquid viscosity (9), corrected to match predicted (10) data for the propane–propylene sys-tem. The value from the plot (9) was increased by a factor required to make the efficiency of the propane–propylene binary distillation equal to 100%. Costs were calculated by the Venture Analysis method (11), because this method yields the appropriate weighting factors for the fixed and operating costs in order to calculate the total costs. Results are ex-pressed as annual costs, before taxes. The important process variables are discussed below.

Operating Temperature. The important temperatures for economic analysis are the overhead condenser temperatures at which heat is re-moved from the process and the reboiler temperatures at which heat is supplied to the process. Of similar importance is the temperature of the solvent-addition plate of the primary column since this temperature, together with that of the recovery column, establishes the temperature swing in the solvent circuit.

One method for fixing the various temperatures is to specify the overhead condenser temperatures in the two columns. In these calcu-lations, it was decided to use cooling water in the two condensers, thereby setting the reflux temperature at 100°F for both columns. The condenser temperature would normally be set by the availability of an adequate heat sink, if other than water. For binary distillation, the reflux tempera-ture was also set at 100°F.

The condenser temperature of 100°F corresponds to a pressure of 187 psia in the primary column and 222 psia in the secondary tower. The recovery column reboiler temperature then comes to 495°F, while the extractive distillation column reboiler temperature varies from about 300° to 425°F. The temperature of the solvent-addition plate in the main tower varied from 100° to 220°F.

Solvent Loading. The solvent circulation rate is a function of the reflux ratio in the primary tower and the liquid-phase concentration of the solvent. For a given solvent selectivity, as the solvent concentration rises, the propane–propylene relative volatility increases and hence the required reflux rate falls. The increased relative volatility results in a decreased number of equilibrium stages required for the desired separa-tion. Figure 4 shows the effect of solvent concentration on the number

Table II.   Cost Calculation Basis

Materials = all steel construction

Tower plates = sieve trays
costs = Peters and Timmerhaus (*12*), Figure 15–26, p. 659

Heat exchangers = floating-head, ¾-inch tubes, 20-ft-long bundle
costs = Peters and Timmerhaus, Figure 14–15, p. 566

Utilities

High pressure steam (500 psig) = \$1.00/10^6 BTU

Low pressure steam (100 psig) = \$0.40/10^6 BTU

Cooling water =   \$0.02/1000 gal

Solvent =   \$5 to 15/lb mole

Tower and heat exchanger sizing procedures = Peters and Timmerhaus
Venture Analysis (*11*):

$$V = P - i_m I_f - i I_w$$

$$P = R - (R - dI_f)t - l_d I_f$$

$$R = S - C$$

$$\therefore V = S - C - (S - C - dI_f)t - (l_d + i_m)I_f - i I_w$$

where
V = venture profit
P = net profit
i_m = rate of return on high risk investment, 20%
I_f = fixed capital investment
i = average rate of return on investment, 12%
I_w = working capital, 15% of fixed capital investment
R = gross profit
d = straight line depreciation factor, 0.1
t = corporate income tax, 50%
l_d = sinking fund depreciation rate, 0.05
S = sales revenue
C = manufacturing cost, utilities + maintenance

maintenance = 6% of fixed capital investment

$$V = 0.5\ S - 0.5\ C + 0.22\ I_f$$

therefore adjusted venture cost

$$= C + 0.44\ I_f = C_u + 0.50\ I_f$$

where
C_u = cost of utilities
I_f = 4.83 I_p (Peters and Timmerhaus, Table 17, p. 118)
I_p = purchased equipment cost

therefore the adjusted venture cost, before taxes, is given by

$$C_u + 2.42\ I_p$$

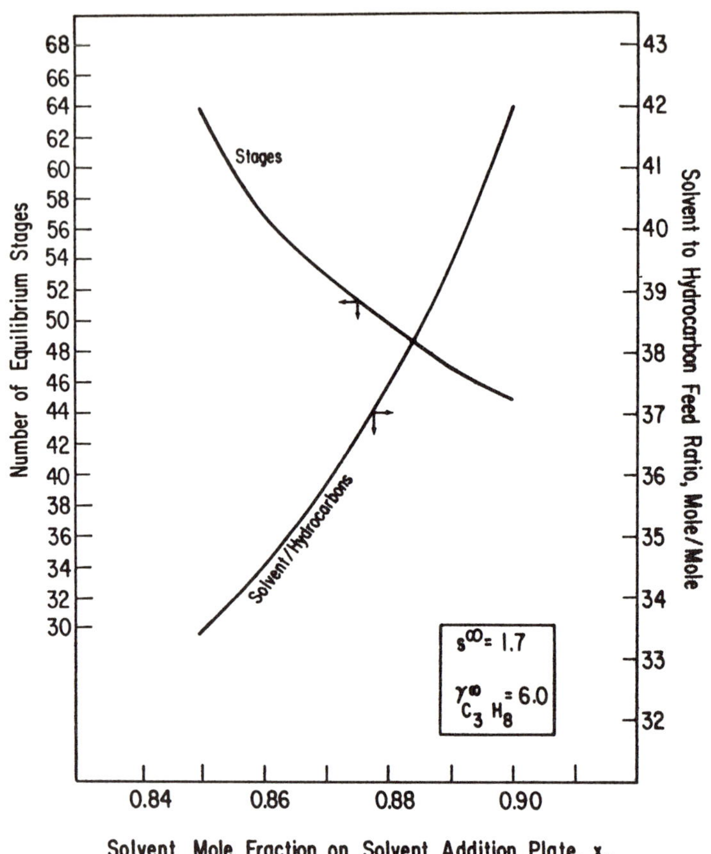

Figure 4.   Effect of solvent concentration on the number of equilibrium stages and the solvent-to-feed ratio in primary column

of stages required and on the solvent-to-hydrocarbon feed ratio needed
for a solvent selectivity $S^\alpha = 1.7$.

A rise in solvent concentration decreases the reflux ratio in the primary column, thereby lowering the vapor flow rate in the column. Consequently, the tower diameter falls. Also, the increased cooler duty is
accompanied by enhanced reboiler duties, resulting in larger utility costs.

With rising solvent concentration, the main tower cost declines, but
the solvent–cooler cost and the utility cost increase. The net result is
shown by the solid lines in Figure 5 where the costs are represented as
fixed, operating, and total costs. A compromise must be made between the
tower costs and the cooler and utility costs to determine the optimum
solvent concentration.

Selectivity and Activity Coefficients. The solvent selectivity determines the relative volatility of the propane–propylene system, with a higher selectivity yielding a higher relative volatility of propane to propylene. An increasing selectivity therefore results in a smaller reflux ratio and fewer equilibrium stages required for the separation. The lower reflux rate corresponds to a lower vapor-flow rate in the tower and hence to a thinner tower. The lower reflux rate also results in a smaller solvent-flow rate with a consequent decrease in the solvent–cooler size and duty and in the reboiler duties.

However, as shown by the plot in Figure 3, the propane activity coefficient increases with rising selectivity. The propane activity coefficient primarily establishes the number of equilibrium stages in the topmost section of the main tower. The higher the activity coefficient, the higher the vapor-phase concentration of the solvent and consequently

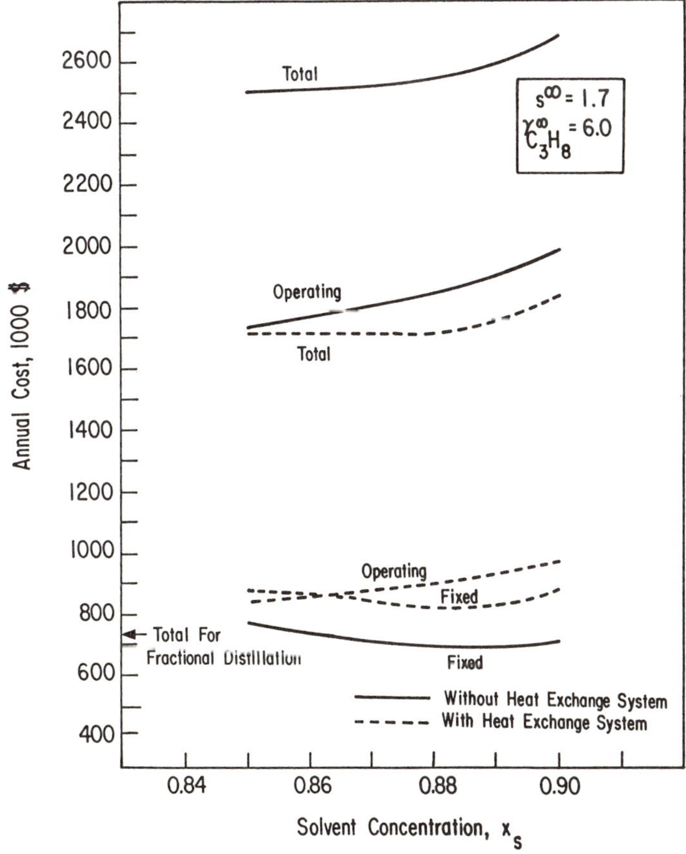

Figure 5.   Effect of solvent concentration on annual costs

the greater the number of stages above the solvent addition plate. For instance, when $\gamma^{\infty}_{C_3H_8} = 6.0$, six stages are required in the topmost section, whereas when $\gamma^{\infty}_{C_3H_8} = 16.0$, 24 stages are needed. Moreover, reverse fractionation occurs in the topmost section of the main column because, in the absence of the solvent, propylene is more volatile than propane and therefore tends to go overhead. The greater the number of stages in the top section, the greater is the extent of this reverse fractionation; the rectifying section must fractionate to a higher propane purity, and thus it needs more stages. A high propane activity coefficient tends to increase the equilibrium stage requirements.

Changes in relative volatility and activity coefficients with changing selectivity act against each other in affecting the equilibrium-stage requirements of the main column. The net result is shown in Figure 6 where the total number of equilibrium stages in the main column is

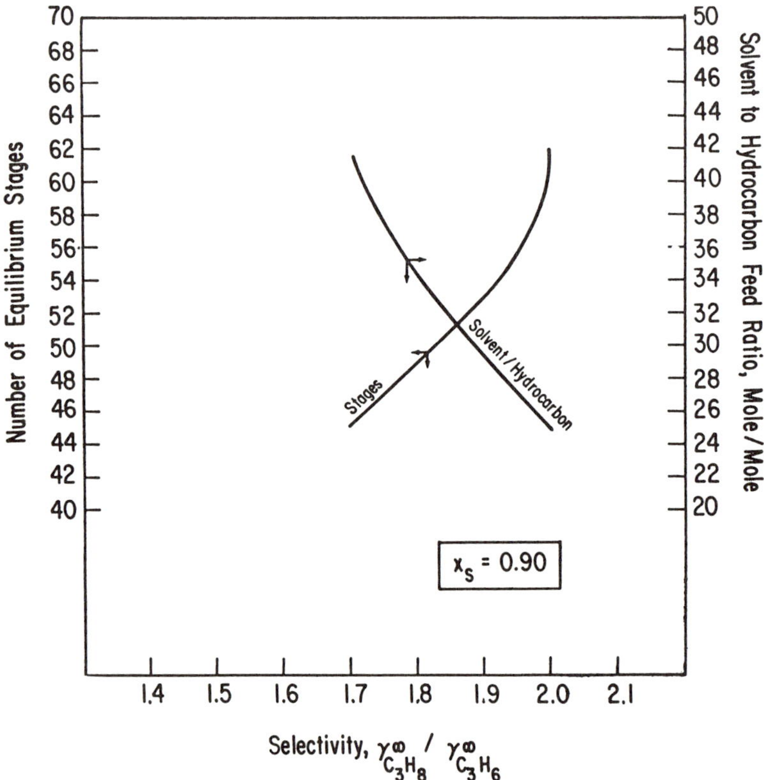

Figure 6.   *Variation of the number of equilibrium stages and solvent/ feed ratio in the primary column with selectivity*

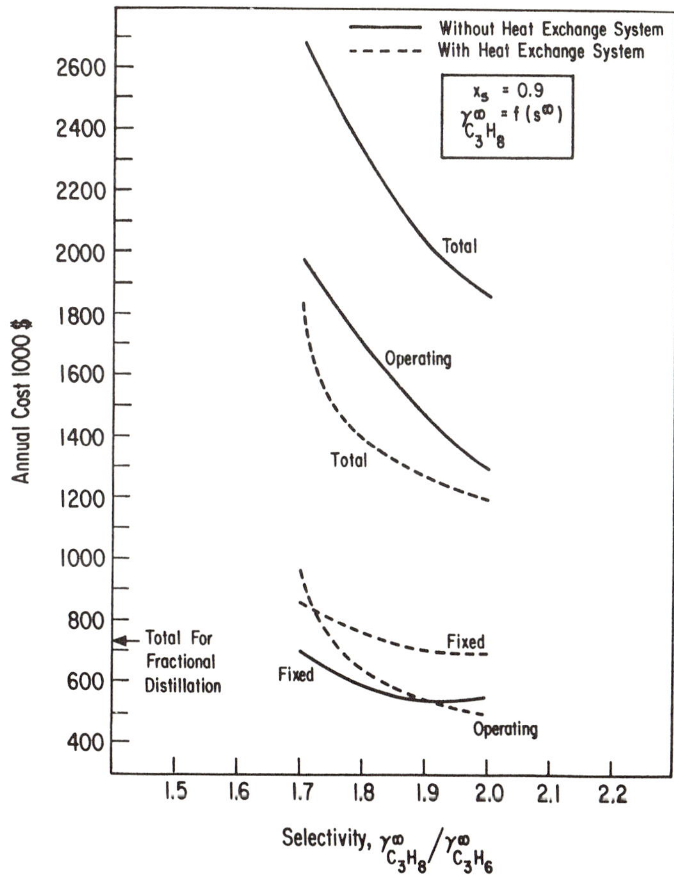

Figure 7.   Effect of solvent selectivity on annual costs

plotted against solvent selectivity. The effect of selectivity on the solvent-to-hydrocarbon ratio is also shown in Figure 6.

A higher selectivity requires a thinner but taller tower. It also requires a smaller solvent cooler because of the lower solvent circulation rate and smaller cooler and reboiler heat duties. The net result is shown in Figure 7 where the solid lines indicate the annual costs as a function of selectivity; they show a falling annual cost with increasing selectivity.

Process Modifications

Figures 5 and 7 show that the operating costs constitute a large fraction of the total annual cost of the extractive distillation process. It is therefore desirable to modify the basic process to reduce these costs.

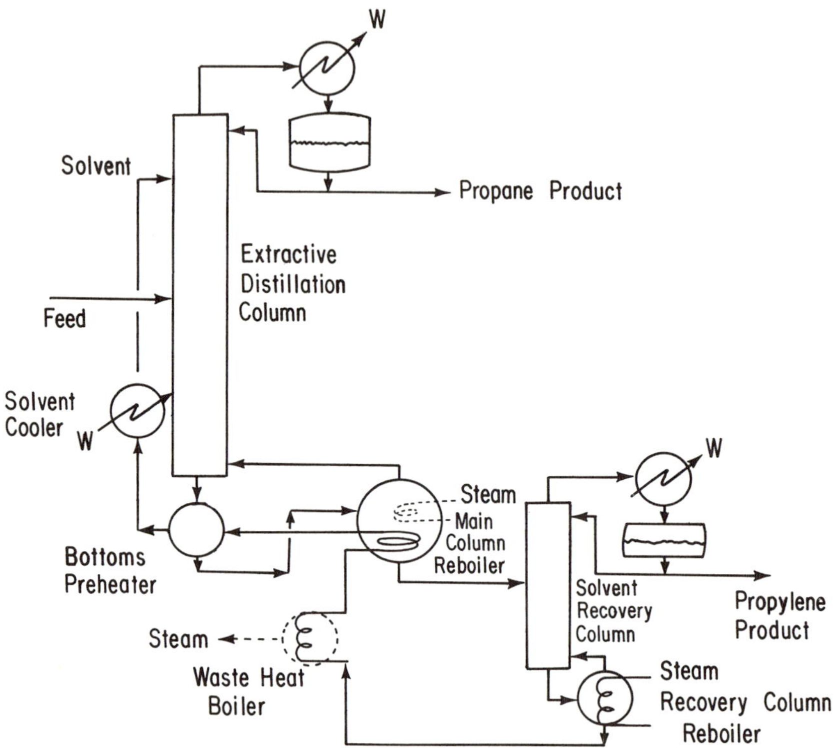

Figure 8.   Extractive distillation with heat recovery

One process modification is shown in Figure 8. In this modification, a heat recovery system uses the heat of the recovery column bottoms in the main column reboiler and in a bottoms preheater. If additional heat is needed in the main column reboiler, auxiliary heating is provided as shown by the (dotted) steam coil in Figure 8. However, a waste heat boiler is sometimes needed (shown dotted) to remove the excess heat in the recovery column bottoms.

Cost calculations were made for this modified extractive distillation process; they are shown by the dashed curves on Figures 5 and 7. The proposed heat exchange system provides considerable reduction in the annual costs of the extractive distillation process. However, the extractive distillation costs are still greater than those for a binary propane–propylene distillation process as indicated on Figures 5 and 7.

The design calculations described in the preceding paragraphs have been made using the functional relation between selectivity and activity coefficient found by Gerster *et al.* (5). However, the data from Hafslund (6), shown in Figure 3, indicate that this relation may not necessarily hold for all solvents. To investigate the effects of increasing selectivity without a corresponding increase in the propane activity coefficient, process calculations were made for various selectivities at a constant propane activity coefficient. Costs were calculated for the process illustrated in Figure 8; they are shown in Figure 9. The costs decrease with increasing selectivity, and the total extractive distillation process cost is approximately the same as that for binary distillation for propane–propylene at a selectivity of 2.6.

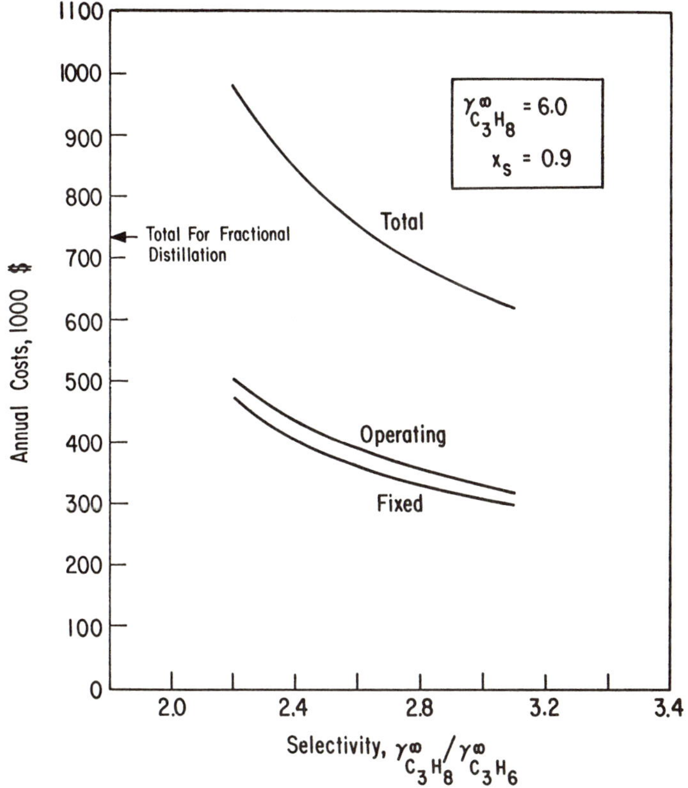

Figure 9.   Effect of solvent selectivity on annual costs at constant propane activity coefficient (process with heat exchange system)

Other process modifications may also be investigated. For example, Figure 10 shows an extractive distillation process with an alternate method for solvent recovery. Here, the main column bottoms are flashed to a pressure low enough for the solvent to cool to the solvent-feed temperature in the main column. Besides decreasing the heat duty of the solvent

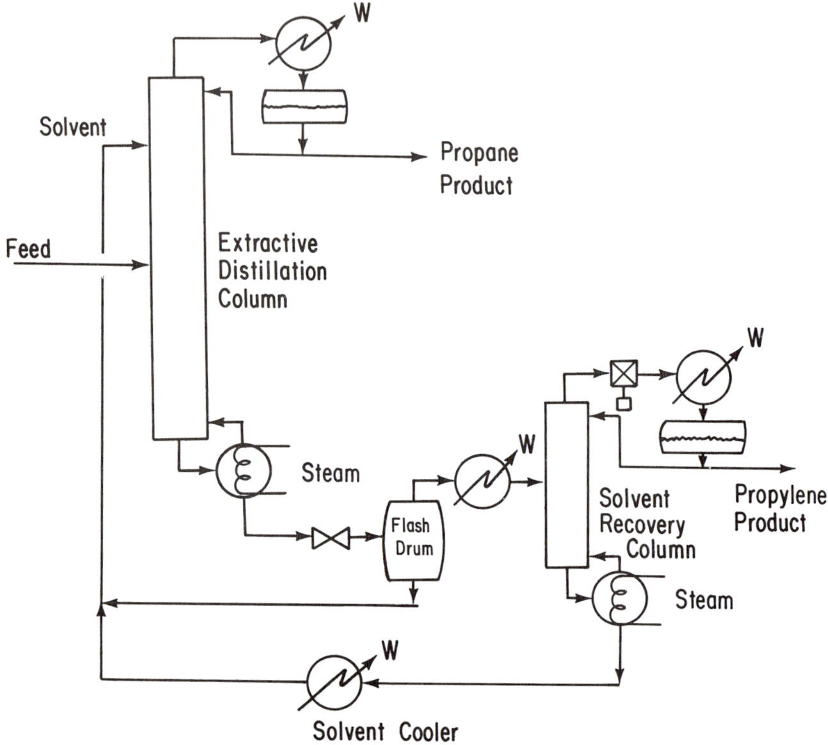

Figure 10.   Extractive distillation with alternate solvent recovery

cooler, this modification also lowers the amount of feed to the recovery column and hence leads to a smaller secondary tower. However, such a modification requires vapor compression or refrigeration to provide reflux for the recovery column.

Conclusions

The costs of separating paraffin–olefin mixtures by extractive distillation are greatly affected by the solvent selectivity, the paraffin activity coefficient, and the solvent volatility; they depend mostly upon solvent characteristics. For a solvent to be effective to separate key components A and B, the solvent must have a high value of $\gamma^{\infty}_A/\gamma^{\infty}_B$ while it must also have a low γ^{∞}_A. Further, the solvent vapor pressure should be lower, but not several orders of magnitude lower, than that of the less volatile hydrocarbon.

For the propane–propylene–solvent system, for the solvents exhibiting the functional relationship between S^{∞} and $\gamma^{\infty}_{C_3H_8}$ shown in Figure 3, it does not seem likely that extractive distillation costs can be reduced below those of binary fractional distillation. Figure 7 shows decreasing costs with increasing selectivity but the slope of the curve of cost *vs.* S^∞ seems to be flattening out at S^∞ of about 2, where extractive distillation costs are still about 65% greater than the costs for binary distillation. However, for solvents which give a high selectivity at relatively lower $\gamma^\infty_{C_3H_8}$, Figure 9 shows a cost *vs.* S^∞ curve which indicates a lower cost for the extractive distillation process at a solvent selectivity higher than about 2.6.

It is evident therefore that the thermodynamic characteristics (S^∞, $\gamma^\infty_{C_3H_8}$, S, $\gamma_{C_3H_8}$, etc.) of the propane–propylene–solvent system are most important in determining the economics of extractive distillation for this separation. Accurate prediction (or experimental determination) of these factors is essential for economic analysis of an extractive distillation process.

Hafslund (6) reports that extractive distillation has been used commercially in one particular case to separate propane–propylene. The feed to the separation process was the off-gas from a reactor in a new process for making acrylonitrile and consisted of 40 wt % inerts, 39 wt % C_3H_6, 8 wt % C_3H_8, 7 wt % acrylonitrile, 5 wt % water, and 1 wt % by-product impurities. The propylene was to be recovered for recycle to the reactor, and the propane and inerts were to be purged from the system. Acrylonitrile was chosen as the solvent for extractive distillation. The topmost section of the primary column was replaced by a water scrubber to recover the acrylonitrile in the vent gas. The process reported by Hafslund (6) is therefore somewhat different from the processes illustrated in Figures 1, 8, and 10.

Extractive distillation is commercially used for separating mixtures of butanes, butenes, butadienes, and various acetylenes with four carbon atoms (13). Separating these multicomponent mixtures by fractional distillation is very difficult because the natural volatilities of the various components, paraffinic as well as olefinic, overlap considerably. For instance, *n*-butane is less volatile than 1-butene but more volatile than *cis*- and *trans*-2-butenes. Thus, separation of butanes from butenes is more difficult by fractional distillation than by extractive distillation where the solvent increases the volatilities of all the butanes to make them greater than the butene volatilities. For 1,3-butadiene recovery extractive distillation is also more attractive than ordinary distillation because the large polarizability of the conjugated double bonds interacts strongly with the polar solvent. Also, in C_4 hydrocarbon separations the solvent often only enhances and does not reverse the natural relative volatility for many of the components; however, even for those components for which the relative volatility is reversed by the solvent, the solvent-free relative volatility is closer to unity than is that of propylene to propane in the absence of solvent. All these factors combine to explain why extractive distillation is relatively more attractive for C_4 hydrocarbon mixtures than for C_3 hydrocarbon mixtures.

Acknowledgment

For financial support the authors are grateful to the National Science Foundation. This work is based, in part, on a previous unpublished study by E. M. Barrish (University of California, Berkeley, 1964).

Literature Cited

1. Prausnitz, J. M., "Molecular Thermodynamics of Fluid-Phase Equilibria," p. 193, Prentice-Hall, Englewood Cliffs, N. J., 1969.
2. Tassios, D., *Chem. Eng.* (1969) **76** (3), 118.
3. Weimer, R. F., Prausnitz, J. M., *Hydrocarbon Process. Petrol. Refiner* (1965) **44** (9), 237.
4. Pierotti, G. T., Deal, C. H., Derr, E. L., *Ind. Eng. Chem.* (1959) **51**, 95.
5. Gerster, J. A., Gorton, J. A., Eklund, R-B., *J. Chem. Eng. Data* (1960) **5**, 423.
6. Hafslund, E. R., *Chem. Eng. Progr.* (1969) **65** (9), 58.
7. King, C. J., "Separation Processes," Ch. 10, McGraw-Hill, New York, 1971.
8. Reamer, H. H., Sage, B. H., *Ind. Eng. Chem.* (1951) **43**, 1628.
9. Treybal, R. E., "Mass Transfer Operations," 2nd ed., p. 151, McGraw-Hill, New York, 1968.
10. American Institute of Chemical Engineers, "Bubble-Tray Design Manual," p. 63, New York, 1958.
11. Rudd, D. F., Watson, C. C., "Strategy of Process Engineering," p. 80, Wiley, New York, 1968.
12. Peters, M. S., Timmerhaus, K. D., "Plant Design and Economics for Chemical Engineers," 2nd ed., McGraw-Hill, New York, 1968.
13. Happel, J., Cornell, P. W., Eastman, DuB., Fowle, M. J., Porter, C. A., Schutte, A. H., *Trans. Amer. Inst. Chem. Eng.* (1946) **42**, 189.

RECEIVED November 24, 1970.

3

Extractive Distillation by Salt Effect

WILLIAM F. FURTER

Department of Chemical Engineering, Royal Military College of Canada, Kingston, Ontario

A salt dissolved in a mixed solvent is capable, through such effects on the structure of the liquid phase as preferential association and others, of altering the composition of the equilibrium vapor. Hence salt effect on vapor-liquid equilibrium relationships provides a potential technique of extractive distillation. A review is presented of the use of dissolved salts, rather than liquid solvents, as separating agents for extractive distillation.

When a salt is dissolved in a boiling solution of two liquid components, there are several salt effects that may occur. These include altering of the boiling point, the mutual solubilities of the two liquid components in each other, and the composition of the equilibrium vapor phase. This paper discusses the latter effect.

The technique of using a salt rather than a liquid as a separating agent for extractive distillation is not new, but such processes have not been widely used. The technology has tended to be proprietary, and the chemistry involved has not been well understood. Also the systems where a dissolved solid separating agent can be applied are limited in number by solubility restrictions. Literature relating to this technique and its chemistry has tended to be fragmentary rather than interrelated, and much of it has not been widely circulated. There is now good evidence to show that this technique should receive more attention.

For such a process the flowsheet is basically the same as that for a normal extractive distillation. The only real difference is that the separating agent is a salt instead of a liquid. Since a dissolved salt is nonvolatile, all of it is contained in the liquid phase, and all of it will flow downward in the column. Hence, for it to occur throughout the column, it must be fed at or near the top. The normal place is in the reentering

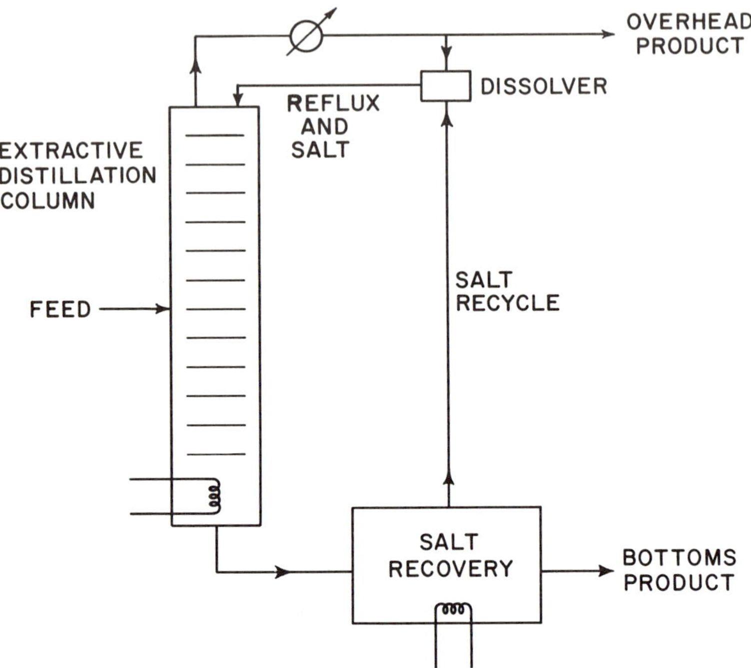

*Figure 1.   Flowsheet for extractive distillation using a dissolved salt
as the separating agent*

reflux stream, as shown in Figure 1. The salt, which must be soluble to
some extent in both liquid components, is fed by dissolving it at a steady
rate into the hot reflux just before reentering the column. It is then
removed from the bottoms product for reuse, as is a liquid separating
agent, but here it is recovered by evaporating or drying instead of by a
subsequent rectification step. The introduction, use, recovery, and recycle
of the separating agent otherwise is the same for a dissolved salt as it is
for a liquid solvent.

In the simplest case the chemical system involved would be a feed
solution consisting of two volatile components (the key components),
which are to be separated from each other, and an added separating
agent (the third component), which circulates internally within the
process. Using the rectification of ethyl alcohol–water mixtures as an
example, current industrial processes use separating agents such as benzene, toluene, or 1-pentane in azeotropic distillation or ethylene glycol in
extractive distillation. In the technique described here, one of several
effective salts capable of eliminating the ethanol–water azeotrope, would
be used as the separating agent in an extractive distillation to concentrate
ethanol–water solutions to absolute alcohol. An example of a particularly

effective salt with this system is potassium acetate; there are several others.

Besides using a single dissolved salt as the separating agent, there are other ways and combinations in which salt is used. For example, the separating agent could consist of a mixture of two or more salts, or one or more salts added to a liquid separating agent to make it more effective and to reduce the amount of the liquid needed, or one or more salts dissolved in an inert liquid solvent which acts only as a carrier for the salt. All possibilities have either been used or considered in various applications of this technique. However, only the simplest case, that in which the separating agent consists only of one component, a single salt, is discussed here.

Advantages and Disadvantages

Why use a dissolved salt instead of a liquid as a separating agent for extractive distillation? First we will consider the disadvantages. A liquid is superior to a solid when considering ease of transport about the system, degree of solubility in the feed components, and rate of mixing at its feedpoint. Liquids mix quickly, but a salt has to dissolve first. There are also mechanical problems to be overcome in metering a finely-divided solid at a constant rate to a boiling or near boiling liquid mixture, and it may also be difficult to achieve rapid dissolving of the salt after it has been fed. Because of solubility limitations restricting the choice of a salt, it is also more probable that a liquid agent, rather than a solid, which is effective and soluble will exist for a given system.

However, in the relatively limited number of systems for which there is a salt which is soluble and effective, some major advantages over a liquid separating agent exist. The salt, being completely nonvolatile, exists only in the liquid phase, and all of it flows down the column and out in the bottoms product. A principal advantage is that the overhead product, provided normal precautions are taken against entrainment, will be completely free of separating agent. Hence there is no need for another section of column (a solvent knockback section) to be located above the feed point of the separating agent to strip separating agent from the overhead product stream, as there is for a liquid agent. Also, less energy is required for the operation since not even part of the separating agent is vaporized and condensed in its cycle through the extractive distillation column, as it would be if it were a liquid.

Another principal advantage is that the effect can be large, sometimes much larger than is possible with liquid separating agents. This is because much stronger forces of association with feed component molecules can be exerted by salt ions than by molecules of a liquid agent.

The result is that much less separating agent would normally be needed; perhaps only a few percent as compared with the typical 50–90% of the liquid phase which is common for separating agent concentration in extractive distillation operations using liquid third components. A reduced requirement in separating agent concentration allows savings to be made in reduced column diameter, reduced recovery and recycle capacity for the separating agent, and reduced energy required for the recovery and recycle step.

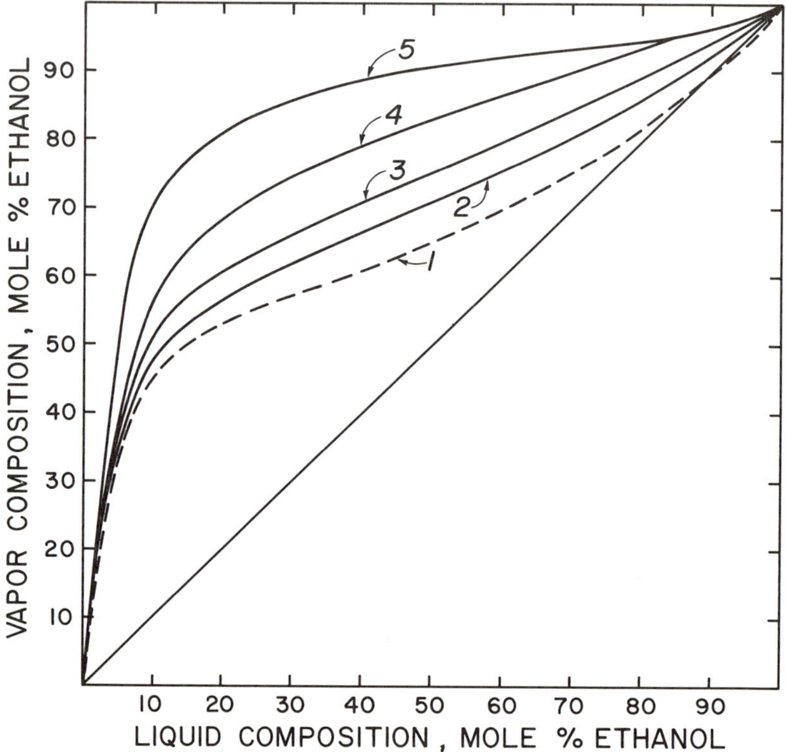

Figure 2.   Vapor–liquid equilibrium data at atmospheric pressure for the boiling ethanol–water system containing potassium acetate at saturation and at various constant concentrations

To illustrate how large the effect of a dissolved salt can be, Figure 2, calculated from the data of Meranda and Furter (1), is included to demonstrate by how much potassium acetate alters the vapor–liquid equilibrium relationship of the system, boiling ethanol–water at atmospheric pressure. The dotted curve represents the ethanol–water system alone, where the azeotrope occurs at about 87 mole % ethanol. The other curves are for various concentrations of potassium acetate, and all are calculated on a salt-free basis to provide a common basis for comparison. The upper curve, labelled #5 in the figure, is for saturated potassium acetate dissolved in the liquid phase. Its saturation concentration—*i.e.,* its solubility—ranges from 49 mole % in pure boiling water down to 10 mole % in pure boiling ethanol, and it increases relative volatility over much of the range shown by a factor of four or five times. The intermediate curves, labelled #2, 3, and 4, are for salt concentrations held constant at 5, 10, and 20 mole % respectively. Even small concentrations of this particular salt completely eliminate the azeotrope.

Figure 3, taken from the data of Dobroserdov (2), gives another example of the substantial effect that a salt, even at reasonably moderate concentration, can have in certain systems. The key components are again ethanol and water, but here the salt is calcium chloride, present at a constant concentration of 10 grams/100 ml of alcohol–water solution. The azeotrope has been completely eliminated, and relative volatility increased substantially.

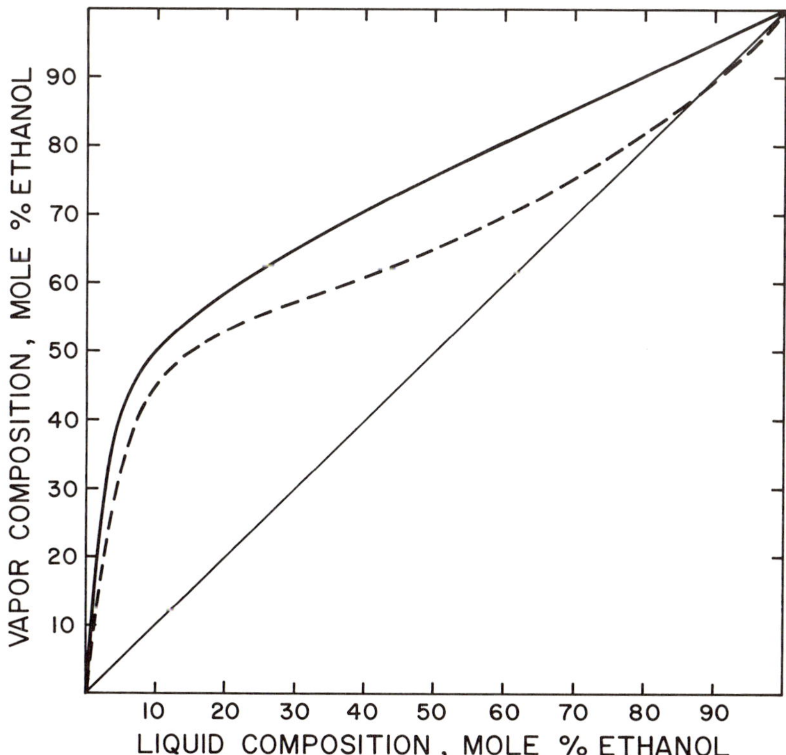

Figure 3. Vapor–liquid equilibrium data at atmospheric pressure for the boiling ethanol–water system containing calcium chloride at constant concentration

Although most previous investigators of salt effect in vapor–liquid equilibrium have used saturated rather than constant salt concentrations to measure the largest salt effect possible at each value of liquid composition for a given salt in a given system, this condition is not representative of salt concentration in an extractive distillation column using dissolved salt as the separating agent. Molal salt concentration in the liquid phase would remain essentially constant from tray to tray within each of the rectifying and stripping sections just as constant as the assumption of constant molal overflow is valid. From a knowledge of salt effect at saturation, however, its effect at a constant concentration below saturation is calculated using the salt effect equation (3, 4).

Chemistry of the Salt Effect

In extractive distillation an added separating agent can modify the vapor–liquid equilibrium relationship of the components to be separated if it can achieve selective molecular association with one of the key components over the other in the liquid phase. The molecules of a liquid separating agent or the ions of a salt tend to form association complexes more with the molecules of one of the feed components to be separated than with the molecules of the other feed component. It can alter the value of relative volatility and the ease of separation of the system and shift or even eliminate an azeotrope if properly chosen. Since the added agent probably complexes to some extent with both key components, the volatilities of both will most likely tend to be lowered, but by differing amounts depending on how selective the agent is in its preference for complexing with one key component over the other. Since a separating agent for extractive distillation normally is chosen so that it prefers the less volatile of the feed components, the value of relative volatility is actually increased by the agent even though the individual volatilities of both feed components may have been reduced in value.

The earliest references to the phenomenon of a salt in the liquid influencing vapor composition go back to the 13th century AD when chemists experimenting with the distillation of alcohol from fermented mash recorded that the presence of potassium carbonate in the still pot enriched the alcohol content of the vapor (5). Most of the work done in the field of salt effect in distillation is grouped into three general categories: salt effect on vapor–liquid equilibrium, extractive distillation using dissolved salts as separating agents, and solution theory of electrolytes—e.g., dissolved salts—in mixed solvents of two or more components. The first two categories have tended to interest chemical engineers and chemists, while the third, generally neglecting the effect on vapor composition, has primarily interested physical chemists. All three categories, however, are interrelated.

Kablukov (*6, 7, 8*) in 1891 and Miller (*9*) in 1897 observed the effects of various salts, dissolved in the liquid phase, on the vapor–liquid equilibrium relationship of the system ethanol–water. Most of the salts they investigated were more soluble in water than in ethanol, and these were observed to enrich the equilibrium vapor in ethanol. However, one salt, mercuric chloride, which is more soluble in ethanol than in water, has the reverse effect. Both investigators concluded that a salt tended to enrich the vapor phase in that component of the liquid in which it was less soluble. They also observed that the magnitude of the selective effect of a salt—*i.e.*, the amount by which it alters vapor composition—is related to the degree of difference in its solubilities in pure water and pure alcohol. Magnitude of salt effect is also a function of the amount of salt present and is limited by the degree of solubility of the salt in the liquid phase. These basic observations, made on this particular system, have tended to be confirmed as general in other systems by more recent investigators.

The most popular system in which the effects of various salts have been investigated over the years has been that of ethanol–water. Other systems which have been studied are ethylene glycol–water, acetic acid–water, methanol–water, 1- and 2-propanol–water, nitric acid–water, acetone–methanol, 1-octane–propionic acid, phenol–water, and formic acid–water. Aqueous systems have been choices for such studies because of salt solubility considerations.

Literature pertaining to salt effect in vapor–liquid equilibrium and to extractive distillation using salt effect was recently reviewed by Furter and Cook (*10*), and the theory and technical aspects were reviewed by Furter (*11*). Vapor–liquid equilibrium data for 188 systems containing salt were previously compiled by Ciparis (*12*), who has also published a recent book with Dobroserdov and Kogan on the theory and practice of extractive distillation by salt effect (*13*).

The chemistry relating to the use of dissolved salts as separating agents has not yet been fully understood. A principal reason for this is the complexity of effects that the salt can have, and how these can vary not only from system to system but, more significantly, within a given system as the concentrations of any or all of the system components are varied. For the apparently simple system defined earlier, consisting of two volatile components plus a dissolved salt, the salt could theoretically range from fully dissociated into two types of ions to totally associated. If its dissociation is anywhere between these two extremes as it probably is, it exists as three species: two types of ions, plus undissociated salt molecules. All three species contribute to the salt effect on the activity of each volatile component, and their parts are probably all different but are interrelated. Hence, the effect of a salt even in a given system is a function of its degree of dissociation, which in turn is a function of liquid phase composition, which varies from point to point within the rectification column.

The forces which cause association complexes within the liquid phase to form may also differ from system to system and from salt to salt, and can include, for example, forces such as van der Waal forces, electrostatic interactions of attraction and repulsion, hydrogen bonding, or combinations of such forces.

To complicate matters more, the association tendencies of salt ions in forming association complexes with molecules of the feed components, besides altering their volatilities, tend to reduce the solubility of one volatile component in the other. Using the old maxim of physical chemistry that "like dissolves like," the selective complexing of the salt with the molecules of one volatile component over those of the other can be visualized as making the molecules of the two volatile components chemically more dissimilar to each other in solution. The effect can be so great in extreme cases that two liquid phases can be made to form even in boiling solutions of what are normally highly miscible liquids. One example of a system where this has been observed is ethanol–water containing ammonium sulfate dissolved to saturation.

There are other complications. The salt, besides forming association complexes with solution molecules, possibly could also alter or even destroy already-existing self-interactions of the molecules of a volatile component either with themselves or with those of the other feed component. An example is the associated structure in which liquid water and to a lesser extent some alcohols exist. The effects of salt ions on water–water, water–alcohol, and alcohol–alcohol complexing, for example, must be profound at higher salt concentrations, and will vary in a given system with salt concentration and with alcohol–water proportionality in the liquid. Also, associations of several, rather than just pairs, of liquid–phase species may form. The full complexity of what initially seems to be a rather simple system finally becomes evident when it is considered that the sum of individual effects which make up the overall effect of the salt on the composition of the equilibrium vapor even in a given system are functions of the relative proportions of all components present and vary with liquid phase composition over the entire range involved in the separation.

Various theories have been proposed and tested to explain salt effect in vapor–liquid equilibrium, including models based on hydration, internal pressure, electrostatic interaction, and van der Waal forces. Although the electrostatic theory of Debye as modified for mixed solvents has had limited success, no single theory has yet been able to account for or to predict salt effect on vapor–liquid equilibrium from pure-component properties alone. Previous investigators have generally agreed that such effects are caused by a complexity of forces and interactions, no one of which has been found significant enough in relation to all of the others to correlate well other than in extremely limited circumstances.

Nevertheless, this ability of a salt, which is not present in the vapor phase, to alter vapor composition, has not wholly escaped industrial attention although its applications have been relatively limited.

Some Applications

Donald F. Othmer while at Eastman Kodak during the 1920's experimented using salts to concentrate acetic acid (*14*). He also developed an industrial process for distilling acetone from its azeotrope with methanol by passing a concentrated calcium chloride brine down the rectification column (*15*). Pure acetone was condensed overhead, and acetone-free methanol was recovered in a separate still from the brine which was then recycled. The improved Othmer recirculation still (*16*) has been the apparatus generally favored by investigators who have studied the effects of salts on vapor–liquid equilibrium.

Cook and Furter (*17, 18*) reported the results of a semiworks study in which aqueous ethanol feedstocks were fractionated in a 12-tray bubble cap column in an extractive distillation using potassium acetate as the separating agent. A method was developed in which the salt was fed as a granular solid by positive-displacement metering screw to the hot reflux, allowing salt to be fed successfully at a steady rate without backflow or loss of vapor and avoiding any clogging of salt by condensed vapor during feeding. Rapid dissolving of the salt in the reflux was achieved by establishing a fluidized bed of dissolving salt at the salt feedpoint. No entrainment of salt into the overhead product was encountered. The azeotrope was eliminated completely by as little as 5 mole % salt present in the liquid phase, allowing 99.9% + anhydrous alcohol, completely salt-free, to be produced from even relatively dilute feedstocks in the 12-tray column. The low salt concentration required is in striking contrast to the 1:1 to 4:1 range of typical solvent–feed ratio required for this system using liquid separating agents even with highly concentrated ethanol feedstocks.

For many years DEGUSSA in Germany licensed a technique known as the HIAG process (*19, 20*) for distilling absolute ethanol, using mixed acetate salts as the separating agent, in the days when ethanol was used as a fuel upgrading additive in automotive gasolines produced in certain countries. Over 100 such plants were built between 1930 and 1950. Users claimed lower capital costs and lower energy requirements in comparison with conventional processes which use benzene or ethylene glycol as the separating agent, and the 99.8% ethanol produced required no further purifying or solvent knockback to rid it of traces of separating agent.

An example of a commercial extractive distillation operation in current major use using a salt is the concentration of aqueous nitric acid using magnesium nitrate as the separating agent instead of the earlier process which had used a liquid separating agent, sulfuric acid. Principal developers of this process have been Hercules and Tennessee Eastman in the United States and Imperial Chemical Industries in Britain. Hercules, which installed the process at Parlin, N. J., 13 years ago, claims several strong advantages for using magnesium nitrate, a salt, as the separating agent instead of sulfuric acid (21). They report operating costs reduced by half largely through savings in reduced energy requirements, capital costs reduced 30 to 40%, a higher yield of product at higher quality, and less pollution of the atmosphere.

Other industrial applications have existed, and these are reviewed elsewhere (10).

Conclusions

Extractive distillation using a dissolved salt in place of a liquid solvent as the separating agent is an unusual unit operation for application in certain specific systems where relatively small concentrations of salt are capable of altering considerably the vapor–liquid equilibrium relationship. The systems to which the technique is applicable are relatively limited in number by the availability of an effective salt for a given system which is adequately soluble in the system over the composition range involved and is selective. Where applicable, however, the effect can sometimes be very large and as a result can greatly reduce the amount of separating agent required, along with yielding an overhead product completely free of separating agent directly from the top of the column without the requirement for a knockback section. This technique is deserving of more attention than the relative obscurity to which it has been relegated to date.

Acknowledgment

The continued research programs on extractive distillation by salt effect and on salt effect in vapor–liquid equilibrium at the Royal Military College of Canada are supported by the Defence Research Board of Canada, Grant No. 9530-40.

Literature Cited

1. Meranda, D., Furter, W. F., *Can. J. Chem. Eng.* (1966) **44**, 298.
2. Dobroserdov, L. L., Il'yina, V. P., *Tr. Leningradskogo Tekhnol. Inst. Pish-chevoi Prom.* (1956) **13**, 92.
3. Johnson, A. I., Furter, W. F., *Can. J. Chem. Eng.* (1960) **38**, 78.
4. Meranda, D., Furter, W. F., *A.I.Ch.E. J.* (1971) **17**, 38.
5. Lescoeur, H., *Ann. Chim. Phys.* (1896) 9 (7), 541.
6. Kablukov, I. A., *Zh. Russk. Fiz.-Khim. Obshch.* (1891) **23**, 388.
7. Kablukov, I. A., *ibid* (1903) **35**, 548.
8. Kablukov, I. A., *ibid* (1904) **36**, 573.
9. Miller, W. L., *J. Phys. Chem.* (1897) **1**, 633.
10. Furter, W. F., Cook, R. A., *Intern. J. Heat Mass Transfer* (1967) **10**, 23.
11. Furter, W. F., *Chem. Engr. (London)* (1968) **219**, CE 173.
12. Ciparis, J. N., "Data of Salt Effect in Vapour–Liquid Equilibrium," Lithuanian Agricultural Academy, Kaunas, Lithuania, USSR (1966).
13. Ciparis, J. N., Dobroserdov, L. L., Kogan, V. B., "Salt Rectification," Khimiya, Leningrad (1969).
14. Othmer, D. F., personal communication (April, 1969).
15. Othmer, D. F., personal communication to J. P. Hartnett (March 7, 1966).
16. Othmer, D. F., *Anal. Chem.* (1948) **20**, 763.
17. Cook, R. A., Furter, W. F., "Extractive Distillation Employing a Dissolved Salt as Separating Agent," A.I.Ch.E. 63rd National Meeting, St. Louis (Feb. 18-21, 1968).
18. Cook, R. A., Furter, W. F., *Can. J. Chem. Eng.* (1968) **46**, 119.
19. *Intern. Sugar J.* (1933) **35**, 266.
20. "Herstellung von absolutem Alkohol nach dem HIAG-VERFAHREN DER DEGUSSA," Degussa, Deusche Gold-und-Silber-Scheideanstalt, Vormals Roessler, Frankfurt (Main), Germany.
21. *Chem. Eng. News* (June 9, 1958), 40.

RECEIVED November 24, 1970.

4

Rapid Screening of Extractive Distillation Solvents

Predictive and Experimental Techniques

DIMITRIOS P. TASSIOS

Newark College of Engineering, Newark, N. J. 07102

Rapid predictive and experimental techniques for screening extractive distillation solvents are reviewed. In preparing a list of potential solvents the method of Scheibel is recommended for non-hydrocarbon systems; for hydrocarbon systems solvents of high polar cohesive density should be considered. For screening the potential solvents the method of Pierotti, Deal, and Derr is recommended. If it is not applicable, the method of Helpinstill and Van Winkle should be considered next. Finally, reliable screening is accomplished through a simple, rapid technique recently developed that uses gas–liquid chromatography.

Extractive and azeotropic distillation in different types of chemical industry has become more important as more separations of close-boiling mixtures and azeotropic ones are encountered. Extractive distillation is used more because it is generally less expensive, simpler, and can use more solvents than azeotropic distillation. Solvent selection for azeotropic distillation has recently been discussed by Berg (*1*). Therefore, solvent screening for extractive distillation is discussed here.

The ease of separation of a given mixture with key components i and j is given by the relative volatility:

$$\alpha_{ij} = \frac{y_i/x_i}{y_j/x_j} = \frac{\gamma_i P^\circ_i}{\gamma_j P^\circ_j} \tag{1}$$

where x is the liquid phase mole fraction, y is the vapor phase mole fraction, γ is the activity coefficient, and P° is the pure component vapor pressure.

The solvent is introduced to change the relative volatility (α_{ij}) as far away from one as possible. Since the ratio (P°_i/P°_j) is constant for small temperature changes, the only way that the relative volatility is affected is by introducing a solvent which changes the ratio (γ_i/γ_j). This ratio, in the presence of the solvent, is called selectivity (S_{ij}):

$$S_{ij} = [\gamma_i/\gamma_j]_{\text{solvent}} \tag{2}$$

In some cases a significant change in operating pressure, and hence temperature, changes α_{ij} enough to eliminate an azeotrope (2).

Besides altering the relative volatility, the solvent should also be easily separated from the distillation products. Other criteria—e.g., toxicity, cost, etc.—discussed by Van Winkle (2) and others must be considered. Relative volatility enhancement is discussed in this paper.

Selecting the proper solvent by considering this criterion is still based on empirical approaches because of the large nonideality of the resulting mixtures. However, general selection patterns and rapid experimental techniques have been made available through the years. This paper presents a review of some of these methods to facilitate the solvent selection process in the chemical industry. Qualitative aspects are first considered, followed by empirical correlations and rapid experimental techniques.

Qualitative Considerations

Since the type of solutions encountered in extractive distillation involve mixtures of polar compounds or polar with nonpolar ones, the solutions are usually nonideal, and predicting the phase equilibrium from pure component data only is practically impossible. Theoretical and experimental studies through the years, however, have established certain trends which are used to search for and screen potential solvents.

Non-Hydrocarbon Mixtures: The Scheibel Method. Scheibel (3) has suggested that the proper solvent can be found among the members of the homologous series of either key components, i or j (α_{ij} close to one). An example presented by Scheibel (3) best demonstrates this approach. Considering the separation of the methanol–acetone azeotrope, the potential solvents according to this method are presented in Table I. Any member of either homologous series can be used. The reason behind this approach is that while the members of a homologous series form essentially ideal solutions, they form nonideal solutions with the other component. For example while methanol forms essentially ideal solutions with ethanol, 1-propanol, and 1-butanol, acetone forms increasingly nonideal solutions with them. While the partial pressure of methanol decreases in the presence of a higher alcohol, that of acetone increases.

Table I. Potential Solvents for the Acetone[a]–Methanol[b] Separation

Solvent	B.P., °C	Solvent	B.P., °C
Methylethyl ketone	79.6	Ethanol	78.4
Methyl n-propyl ketone	102.0	Propanol	97.8
Methyl isobutyl ketone	115.9	Water	100.0
Methyl n-amyl ketone, etc.	150.6	Butanol	117.0
		Amyl alcohol	137.8
		Ethylene glycol	197.4

[a] Boiling point: 54.6°C.
[b] Boiling point: 64.7°C.

So that an azeotrope with acetone does not form, the alcohol used must have a high enough boiling point. This requirement is reliably established only if vapor–liquid equilibrium data for at least two, preferably three, of the members of the series with acetone are known. The Pierotti–Deal–Derr method (4) (discussed later) or the Tassios–Van Winkle method (5) can be used in this case. In the latter method a log–log plot of γ°_i vs. P°_i should yield a straight line. Figure 1 presents results for n-alcohols and benzene from the isobaric (760 mm Hg) data of Wehe and Coates (6). Reliable infinite dilution activity coefficients are established for the other n-alcohols from data for at least two, and preferably three, of them. These γ° values are used with equations like those of Van Laar or Wilson (7) to generate activity coefficients at intermediate compositions and to check for an existing azeotrope or a difficult separation (x–y curve close to the 45° line).

From the two series the one of the alcohols is preferred because here acetone is the overhead product and using a ketone causes the relative volatility to invert. Scheibel (3) recommends that the lowest boiling homolog, which does not form an azeotrope, is chosen. An alternative approach suggests the homolog which barely meets the miscibility requirement, for this results in high selectivity (8). The choice between these conflicting suggestions must be made on the basis of economical considerations.

Hydrocarbon Mixtures. Here it is usually not the existence of an azeotrope but rather the close vapor pressure of the key components that often necessitates using extractive distillation.

The qualitative criteria for solvent selection for hydrocarbon mixtures have been discussed by Prausnitz and Anderson (9) and Weimer and Prausnitz (10). Since a review was presented recently by Tassios (11), only the conclusions are discussed here.

The types of possible interactions between a mixture of hydrocarbons and a polar solvent are:

1. physical (dispersion and dipole-induced dipole)
2. chemical (resulting from the formation of loosely bound aggregates)

Using physical interaction alone, Prausnitz and Anderson (9) and Weimer and Prausnitz (10) have developed this simplified expression for hydrocarbon selectivity, $S°_{23}$, at infinite dilution in a solvent:

$$ln\ S°_{23} \propto (\tau_1)^2(V_3-V_2) \tag{3}$$

where τ_1 is the polar cohesive energy density of the solvent, which is re-related to the polarity and the molar volume of the solvent. References 10 and 11 explain how to calculate τ. The selectivity is higher, the larger the difference in molar volume between the hydrocarbons and the larger the polar cohesive energy density (τ) of the solvent. Prausnitz and coworkers (9, 10), Gerster and his coworkers (12), Pierroti, Deal, and Derr (13), and Deal and Derr (14) give experimental evidence to support the above conclusions. For example, the selectivities of the pair hexane–benzene at 25°C with various solvents (14) are presented along with the values for τ_1 in Table II and plotted against each other in Figure 2. Here

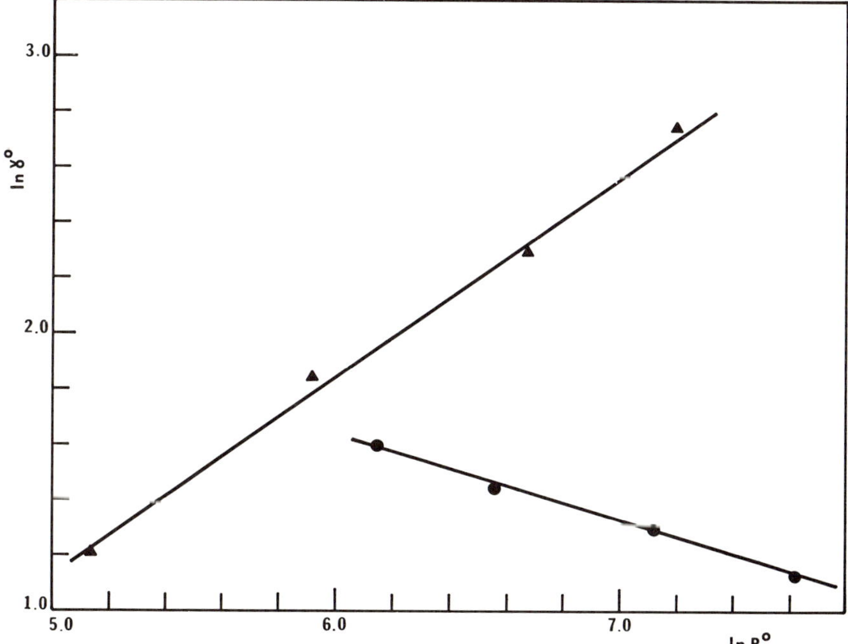

Figure 1.   Prediction of infinite dilution activity coefficients for numbers of a homologous series in a common solvent: n-Alcohols in Benzene at 1 atm

▲ $\gamma°_B$ vs. $P°_B$ ● $\gamma°_A$ vs. $P°_A$

(V_3-V_2) is constant, and the selectivity tends to increase with $\tau_1{}^2$, indicated by Equation 3.

Loosely bound aggregates (chemical effects) are formed with the hydrocarbons acting as electron donors (Lewis base) and the solvents acting as electron acceptors (Lewis acid). The hydrocarbon that forms the most stable complex with the solvent experiences a decrease in volatility. Electron donors are rated by ionization potential, and electron acceptors are rated by their electron affinities. The selectivity will be higher, the larger the difference in ionization potential between the hydrocarbons and the larger the electron affinity of the solvent (9). While data on ionization potentials of hydrocarbons can be found (15, 16), electron affinities data are rare because of difficulties in their experimental determination. Prausnitz and Anderson (8) recommend that the sigma scale, proposed by Hammett (17), be used to determine approximately the solvent's relative ability to form complexes with the two hydrocarbons. Attempts by this author, however, to use this scale were not conclusive. Prausnitz and Anderson (8) should be consulted to understand better the physical and chemical effects.

The Effect of Solvent and Solute Concentration. The effect of solvent concentration on selectivity is qualitatively described by three types (2, 11) shown in Figure 3.

In the first type the selectivity increases almost linearly with solvent concentration, and this seems to represent the predominant pattern (18, 19). In the second type the selectivity increases more than linearly with solvent concentration, but it is halted by immiscibility at high solvent concentrations (20). The third type shows a maximum and is an unusual pattern. One such case was observed by Hess et al. (21) in studying the separation of 1-butane from butenes-2 with the furfural solvent (96.5%

Table II. Selectivities and Polar Cohesive Energy Densities for the Hexane (1)–Benzene (2) System at 25°C (12)

Solvent	$S°_{23}$	$\tau_1(cal/cc)^{1/2}$
MEK	3.6	5.33
Acetone	3.8	6.14
Pyridine	5.2	3.71
Aniline	12.2	6.37
Acetonitrile	9.4	8.98
Propionitrile	6.5	7.17
Nitromethane	15.0	9.44
Nitrobenzene	5.8	4.89
Phenol	6.0	9.84
Furfural	10.9	7.62
Dimethyl-sulfoxide	22.0	9.47
Dimethyl formamide	12.5	8.07

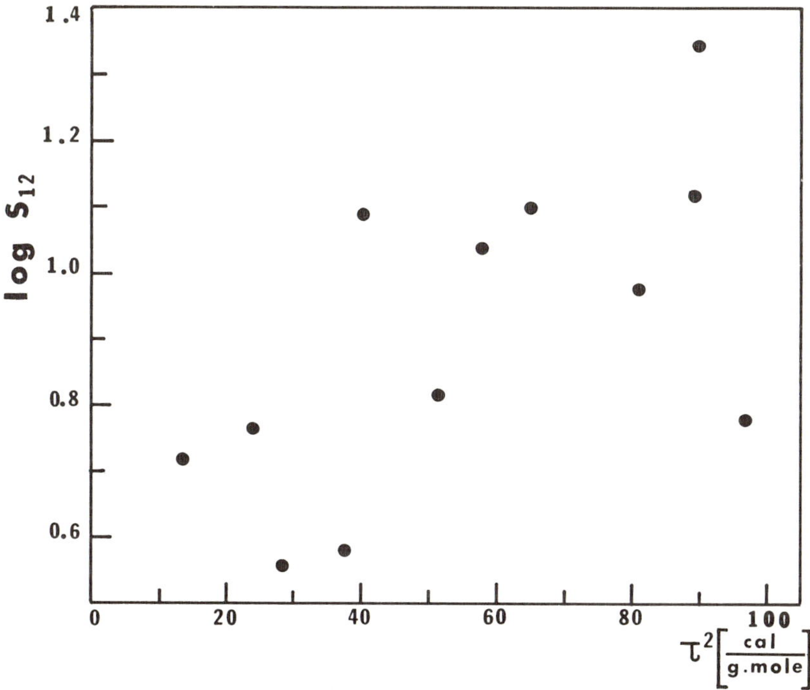

*Figure 2.   Variation of selectivity with solvent's polar cohesive density;
system: hexane (1)–benzene (2) at 25°C (12)*

weight furfural and 3.5% water). However, Gerster *et al.* (*22*) report
that selectivity increased with solvent concentration for the system
butane–butene-1 with pure furfural as solvent. Considering the extensive
experimental work of the second study, the results should be considered
more reliable. Another case involves the separation of ethyl benzene from
ethyl cyclohexane with hexylene glycol as solvent (*23*). The maximum
appears in this case if definite, and the data are reproduced. This decrease
in selectivity at higher solvent concentration results from the higher
temperatures resulting from larger solvent concentration, for as temperature increases, selectivity decreases.

Selectivity is also affected by the relative concentrations of the key
components. If component (1) forms a more nonideal solution with the
solvent than component (2), a decrease in x_1 will affect γ_1 much more
than a decrease of x_2 will affect γ_2. Hence, as x_1 decreases, S_{12} increases
more rapidly than when x_2 decreases. Experimental evidence (*19, 20*)
clearly shows this. For example, consider how propanol affects the relative volatility of the *n*-hexane (1)–benzene (2) system. Hexane forms a

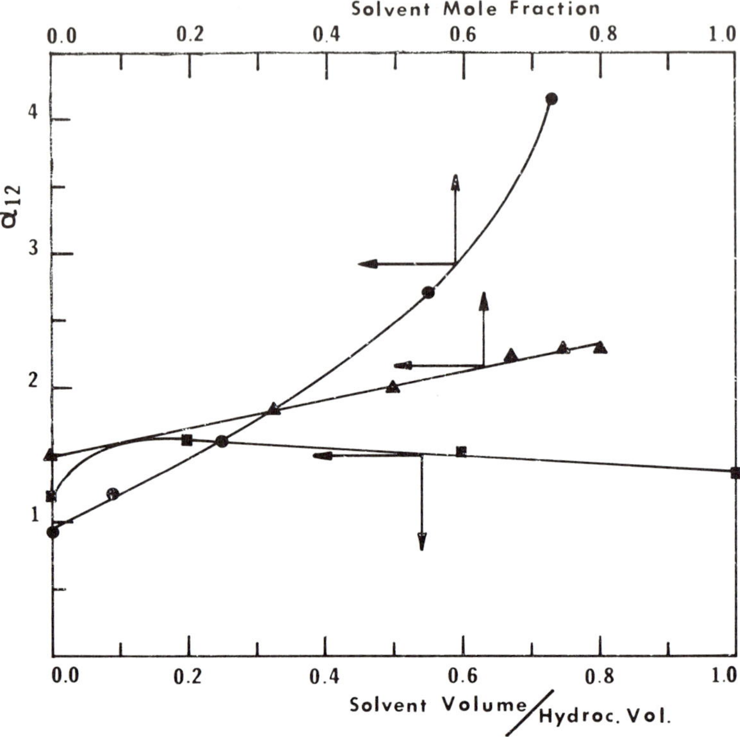

Figure 3. Variation of relative volatility with solvent amount. Hydrocarbon ratio is 1:1. P: Constant.

■ *ethylcyclohexane (1)–ethyl benzene (2)/hexylene glycol* (22)
▲ n-*hexane (1)–benzene (2)/1-propanol* (18)
● *2-4 dimethylpentane (1)–benzene (2)/aniline* (19)

more nonideal system with propanol than benzene (*19*). As the ratio (x_1/x_2) decreases, S_{12} increases. This was observed experimentally (*19*) (*see* Figure 4).

Mixed Solvents Effect. Using mixed solvents can improve selectivity. For example, adding small amounts of water has improved the selectivity of furfural in separating C_4 hydrocarbons (*24*). Baumgarten and Gerster (*25*) have studied how various solvents affect the selectivity of furfural for the pentane–pentene pair. They concluded that for only a few solvents some improvement was observed. The resulting selectivity lies between the selectivity of the pure solvents (*see* Table III). To avoid immiscibility at high solvent concentrations, a second solvent is sometimes added (*25*).

The Effect of Temperature. The temperature effect on selectivity is given by:

$$\frac{d(\log S^{\circ}_{12})}{d(1/T)} = \frac{L^{\circ}_1 - L^{\circ}_2}{2.303R} \qquad (4)$$

where L°_k is partial molar heat of solution, component k at infinite dilution in the solvent.

For hydrocarbon pairs in different solvents and over moderate temperature ranges (to 100°C), a linear dependency of $\log S^{\circ}_{12}$ on $(1/T)$ can be assumed (*12, 14, 26*). An example is shown in Figure 5, where $\log S^{\circ}$ for the hexane–benzene pair in five different solvents is plotted against the reciprocal absolute temperature. The relationship can be considered linear for engineering applications. Selectivity decreases with increasing temperature, and this explains the unusual maximum in the variation of selectivity with solvent concentration shown by the system ethylbenzene–ethyl cyclohexane with hexyleneglycol as solvent (Figure 3).

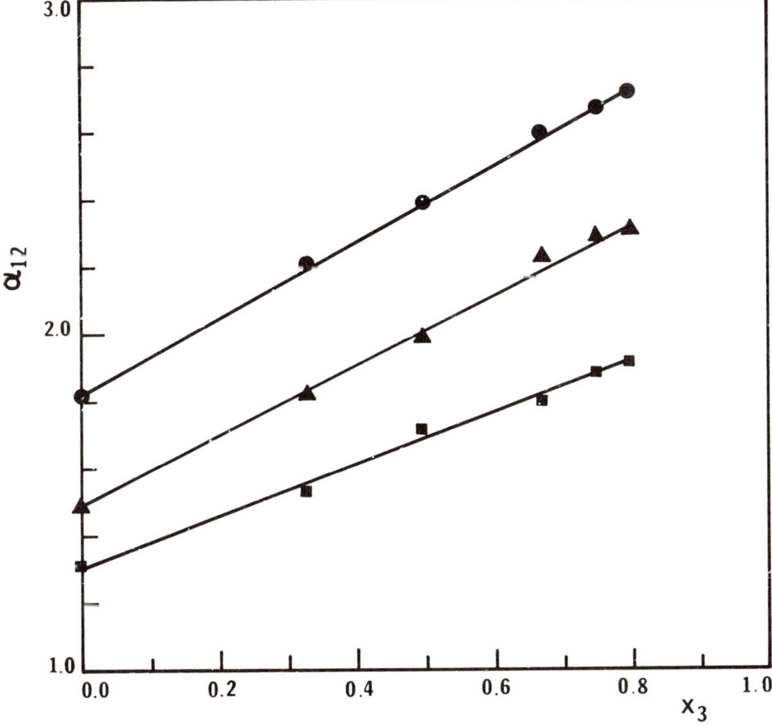

M. Van Winkle, "Distillation," McGraw-Hill

Figure 4.   Variation of relative volatility with composition (2). System: hexane (1)–benzene (2)/1-propanol (3) at 760 mm (18).

x_1/x_2: ● *1:3,* ▲ *1:1,* ■ *3:1*

Table III. Selectivity of Pure and Mixed Solvents

Solute	Mixed Solvents		B,[a] Vol %	S[a]
	A	B		
	Methyl Cellosolve	Nitromethane	0	1.69
	Methyl Cellosolve	Nitromethane	5	1.70
	Methyl Cellosolve	Nitromethane	100	2.49
n-Pentane (3)	Pyridine	-Butyrolactone	0	1.60
	Pyridine	-Butyrolactone	32.1	1.79
1-Pentene (2)	Pyridine	-Butyrolactone	100	2.17
	Ethyl methyl ketone	-Butyrolactone	100	2.17
	Ethyl methyl ketone	-Butyrolactone	50	1.79
	Ethyl methyl ketone	-Butyrolactone	0	1.62
	Acetonitrile	Water	0	1.64
Propane (3)	Acetonitrile	Water	50	1.34
Propylene (2)	Acetonitrile	Water	100	.98

[a] Acetonitrile–water data from Reference *41*, all others from Reference *12*.

Quantitative Methods

Infinite dilution activity coefficients are predicted by several methods (*4, 5, 10, 27, 28, 29, 30, 31*). The most general are the Pierotti–Deal–Derr method (*4*), the parachor method (*27*), and the Weimer–Prausnitz method (*10*), modified by Hellpinstill and Van Winkle (*28*). Since accuracy is limited in these methods and noninfinite dilution conditions prevail in actual operations, the infinite dilution activity coefficients obtained should only be used for screening purposes.

Pierotti-Deal-Derr Method (*4*). Infinite dilution activity coefficients (γ°) of structurally related systems are correlated in this method to the number of carbon atoms of the solute and solvent (n_1 and n_2). For the members of the homologous series $H(CH_2)_{n_1}X_1$ (solute) in the members of the homologous series $H(CH_2)_{n_2}Y_2$:

$$\log \gamma^\circ_1 = A_{1,2} + \frac{F_2}{n_2} + B_2 \frac{n_1}{n_2} + \frac{C_1}{n_1} + D_0(n_1-n_2)^2 \tag{5}$$

where the constants are functions of temperature, B_2 and F_2 are functions of the solvent series, C_1 is a function of the solute series, $A_{1,2}$ is a function of both, and D_0 is independent of both.

For zero members of a series—*e.g.*, water for alcohols—no infinite value for γ° is obtained. Instead, by convention, any terms containing an n for the zero member are incorporated in the corresponding coefficient. So for n-alcohols in water:

$$\log \gamma^\circ_1 = K + B_2 n_1 + C_1/n_1 \tag{6}$$

Notice that the term $D_o\,(n_1 - n_2)^2$ was incorporated into the K constant because D_o is smaller than the other coefficients by a factor of 10^3; therefore, this term is insignificant. In Equation 6 only K is a function of the solute and solvent, as stated before. B_2 is always the same when water is the solvent and C_1 is the same for n-alcohol solutes. This is shown better from the following homologous series in water at 100°C:

$$\left. \begin{array}{l} n\text{-Alcohols:}\quad \log \gamma^\circ_1 = -0.420 + (0.517)\,n_1 + (0.230)/n_1 \\[4pt] n\text{-Aldehydes:}\ \log \gamma^\circ_1 = -0.650 + (0.517)\,n_1 + (0.32)/n_1 \end{array} \right\} \tag{7}$$

The coefficient B is the same in both cases.

Equation 6 assumes a different form for cyclic compounds in a fixed solvent. For unalkylated cyclic (aromatic and/or naphthenic) hydrocarbons in fixed solvents:

$$\log \gamma^\circ_1 = K + B_a n_a + B_n n_n + C_r[1/r - 1] \tag{8}$$

where B_a and B_n are solvent dependent constants, C_r is constant, depending on the type of ring (diphenyllike or naphthalenelike), r is the number of rings, and n_a and n_n are aromatic and napthenic carbon numbers, respectively. For example for diphenyllike hydrocarbons in phenol at 25°C:

$$\log \gamma^\circ_1 = 0.383 + 0.1421\, n_a + 0.2406\, n_n + 1.845[1/r - 1] \tag{9}$$

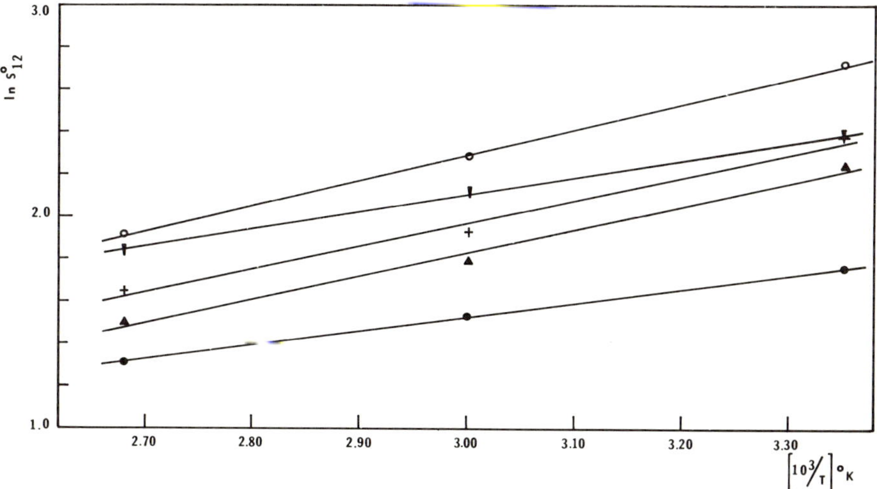

Figure 5.   Dependence of selectivity on temperature. System: hexane (1)–benzene (2). ● nitrobenzene, ▲ acetonitrile, + furfural, ▼ dimethyl sulfolane, ○ diethylene glycol

Correlations for various systems, developed by using experimental data on 265 systems, are available (*11, 26*). The relationships used, the numerical values of the constants, and the calculated and experimental values for γ° are available (*13*) and should be used to study solvent selection.

The Parachor Method (*27*). Infinite dilution activity coefficients are obtained according to this method from the following relationship (*27*):

$$\log \gamma^\circ{}_1 = \frac{1}{2.303RT} [U_1{}^{1/2} - CU_2{}^{1/2}]^2 \tag{10}$$

where U_i is potential energy of component i calculated from: $U_i = (\Delta H_{vap})_i - RT$, ΔH_{vap} is enthalpy of vaporization, cal/gram mole, C is a constant, a function of temperature, the parachor ratio of the two components, and the number of carbon atoms in the solute and solvent molecules; R is the gas constant.

Equation 10 generalizes the expression of Erdös (*31*) applicable to components involving the same functional group. Returning to the constant C in Equation 10, usually the number of carbon atoms does not directly affect the constant. Apparently this effect is corrected by the parachor which changes with the number of carbon atoms. For example, for aromatics in furfural:

$$C = (0.5632 + 0.03 \times 10^{-4}t)\,(P_1/P_2)^{0.2222} \tag{11}$$

and for naphthenes in furfural:

$$\log C = (0.2658 + 14.53 \times 10^{-4}t)\,(\log P_1/P_2 - 0.5982) - 0.2679 \tag{12}$$

where P_i is parachor of component i and t is temperature, °C. About the same variety of systems, covered in the PDD method, is covered in this approach, and the expressions for C are given elsewhere (*27*).

A comparison between the PDD and the parachor method seems to suggest that the latter is no worse than the former, and often better (*27*). For the systems considered, the parachor method gives lower maximum deviations in 11 cases, the PDD in 7. Also, the authors of the parachor method claim better accuracy when extrapolation with respect to temperature is required. For example, the case of *n*-heptane (1) in 1-butanol (2) is cited. Values for γ° calculated by extrapolating the PDD constants to temperatures ranging from 114.5°C–171.9°C yield error ranging from 100–200%; the errors for the parachor method range between 0.5–3.6%. However, this is the only comparison available (*27*) and may not always be valid. The parachor values are estimated for different compounds by a group contribution method (*32, 33*).

The Weimer-Prausnitz (WP) Method (*10*). Starting with the Hildebrand–Schatchard model for nonpolar mixtures (*34*), Weimer and Prausnitz developed an expression for evaluating values of hydrocarbons in polar solvents:

$$\text{RT} \ln \gamma^{\circ}{}_2 = V_2[(\lambda_1 - \lambda_2)^2 + \tau_1{}^2 - 2\psi_{12}] +$$
$$\text{RT}[\ln V_2/V_1 + 1 - V_2/V_1] \tag{13}$$

where V_i is the molar volume of pure i, cc/gram mole, λ_i is the nonpolar solubility parameter, component i, and τ_i is the polar solubility parameter, component i. The subscript 1 represents the polar solvent and subscript 2 is the hydrocarbon solute with

$$\psi_{12} = k^r \tau_1{}^2 \tag{14}$$

Later Helpinstill and Van Winkle (*28*) suggested that Equation 13 is improved by considering the small polar solubility parameter of the hydrocarbon (olefins and aromatics):

$$\text{RT} \ln \gamma^{\circ 2} = V_2[(\lambda_1 - \lambda_2)^2 + (\tau_1 - \tau_2)^2 - 2\psi_{12}] +$$
$$\text{RT}[\ln V_2/V_1 + 1 - V_2/V_1] \tag{13a}$$

Also Equation 14 becomes:

$$\psi_{12} = k(\tau_1 - \tau_2)^2 \tag{14a}$$

The value of k was obtained by curve-fitting experimental infinite dilution activity coefficients of paraffins, olefins, and aromatics in several polar solvents. The value of k for each hydrocarbon group is given in Table IV. The values for λ_i are taken from plots (*28*). The method for calculating τ_i is also available (*28*).

The term ψ_{12} corresponds to the induction energy between the polar and nonpolar, or slightly polar, species. Since no chemical effects are included, the correlation should not be used for solvents showing strong hydrogen bonding.

Rapid Experimental Techniques

The safest method used to choose extractive distillation solvents is to measure directly multicomponent vapor–liquid equilibrium data of the components involved with the solvents being considered. This, however, is a tedious, time consuming approach. There are rapid experimental techniques which can at least be used in the screening stage of selecting the solvent. Two methods are discussed here; both use gas–liquid chromatography, and they are simple and rapid. The first (*35*) is only used to screen; the second (*36*), besides screening, gives infinite dilution relative volatilities. Both methods require a solvent with a lower vapor pressure than the solutes as in extractive distillation.

Table IV.   Values for k in Equation ($14a$)

System	k	% Average Absolute Error in γ°
Paraffins	0.399	11.6
Olefins	0.388	8.5
Aromatics	0.447	13.5

Screening Solvents through GLC. In gas–liquid chromatography (GLC) separating mixture components is based on the partitioning liquid being able to interact with different strengths with them, along with the vapor pressure differences. The same is true for an extractive distillation solvent. It seems logical, therefore, that extractive distillation solvents could be rated on their performance as partitioning liquids with the mixture under consideration.

Warren *et al.* (37) and Sheets and Marchello (38) have suggested using gas–liquid chromatography to study extractive distillation solvents. In the first study (37) an individual column was prepared for each solvent by using this solvent as a partitioning liquid. It is a tedious, time-consuming method and was restricted to solvents of high boiling point. Finally the experimental evidence based on limited data is not conclusive. Sheets and Marchello (38) significantly simplified it by replacing the preparing of individual columns for each solvent with directly injecting the solvent in a chromatograph containing a general purpose column. No experimental evidence was given to support applying GLC to rate extractive distillation solvents. Recently Tassios (35) has proved that the method is effective for screening.

The technique consists of injecting a certain amount (*e.g.*, 3 cc) of the solvent being considered into the chromatograph containing a general purpose column or a column containing an inert support. Next, four or five 5-ml samples of a mixture of the key components are injected, and the separation factor, F_{12}, is measured for each sample:

$$F_{12} = D_2/D_1 \tag{15}$$

where D_i is distance between air peak and peak for component i as shown in Figure 6.

The obtained values of F_{12} for these samples are plotted against time from solvent injection to establish the maximum value for the separation factor, F_{12} (max). Further details about the experimental technique are in the original paper (35). The larger the value of F_{12} (max), the better the solvent can separate the mixture, indicating a better extractive distillation solvent. This was verified by comparing values for F_{12} (max) and infinite dilution relative volatilities (α°_{12}) for the system *n*-hexane–benzene with six different solvents. The results presented in

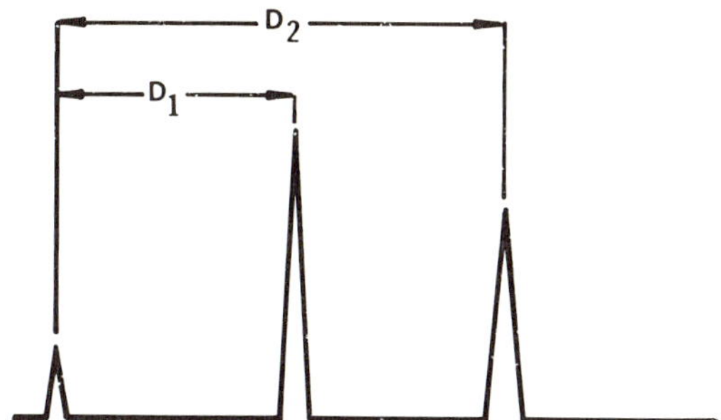

Figure 6.   Evaluation of the separation factor
F_{12}

Table V and plotted in Figure 7 suggest that the larger the value of $\alpha°_{12}$, the larger the value of F_{12} (max). The deviations observed with diethylene glycol must result from the limited solubility of *n*-hexane and benzene in this solvent (35). Comparing the solvents based on the same volume is recommended because it is easier and seems more conclusive.

Infinite Dilution Relative Volatilities through GLC. If the solvent amount injected in the column is high enough so that infinite dilution conditions for the injected solute prevail, it is readily shown (38) that the separation factor becomes equal to the infinite dilution relative volatility:

$$\alpha°_{ij} = \frac{y_i/x_i}{y_j/x_j} = \frac{\gamma°_i P°_i}{\gamma°_j P°_j} = F_{ij} = \frac{D_j}{D_i} \tag{16}$$

Doring (39) has shown that infinite dilution relative volatilities can be evaluated through GLC. He prepared a special column for each solvent under consideration, a tedious project. A year later Sheets and Marchello (38) showed that separation factors increase with increased amounts of injected solvent. Later Tassios (35) found out the same to

Table V.   Separation Factors and Infinite Dilution Relative Volatilities for the System *n*-Hexane (1)–Benzene (2) at 67°C (35)

Solvent	$\alpha°_{12}$	F_{12} [a] 0.03 gram moles	3 cc
Pyridine	3.70	5.85	5.40
Propionitrile	4.80	6.10	6.40
Furfural	6.55	6.40	7.50
Nitromethane	7.00	6.95	7.95
N-methylpyrrolidone	8.20	8.40	8.40
Diethyleneglycol	9.10	4.70	4.50

[a] Calculated for two solvent amounts.

be true but observed that at higher solvent amounts, 5–6 cc for the column used in that study, the separation factor seems to level off approaching the infinite dilution value which was found from static measurements. In a later study Tassios (*36*) used a 6 ft column containing only chromosorb G and a 10 ft column containing glass beads and found that constant values for the separation factor were obtained at solvent levels equal or above 2.0 cc. For four solvents with two hydrocarbon binary mixtures, the separation factor measured at 2 cc of solvent agree well with experimental infinite dilution relative volatilities. The maximum deviation was 23.8%, the minimum 3.1%. This approach of direct solvent injection eliminates the tedious column preparation.

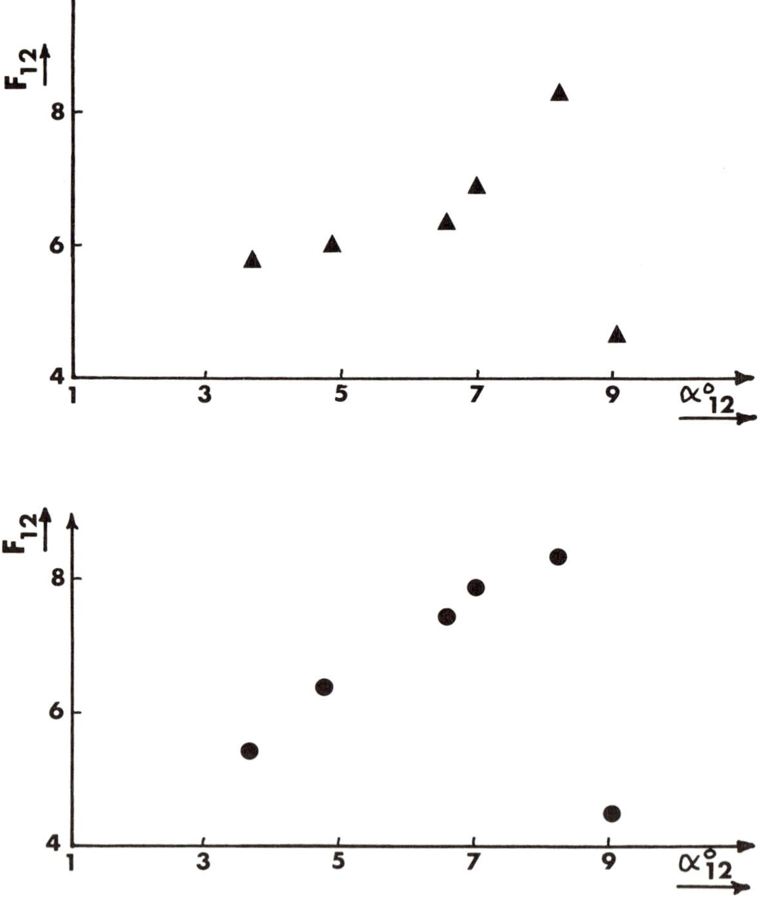

Figure 7. Relationship between maximum separation factors and infinite dilution relative volatilities for the system: n-hexane–benzene with various solvents at 67°C (35)

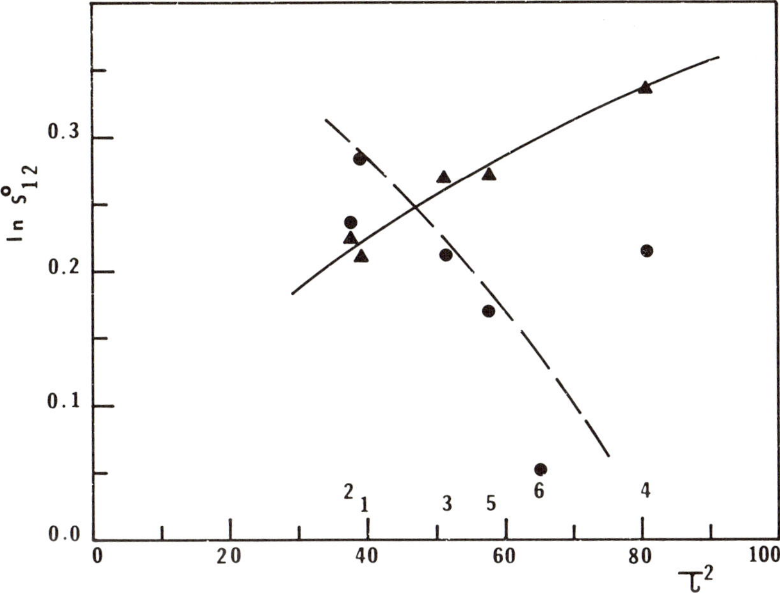

*Figure 8.   Variation of selectivity with solvent's polar cohesive
energy density*

● *propane (1)–propene (2) at 27°C (24)*
△ *pentane (1)–pentene (2) at 25°C (10)*

1. *butyronitrile*	2. *acetone*	3. *propionitrile*
4. *acetonitrile*	5. *furfural*	6. *DMF*

Discussion

The criterion of high solvent polarity should be cautiously applied
(Equation 3) in preparing a list of prospective solvents. There are
exceptions among solvents showing hydrogen bonding which produces
higher values of polar cohesive energy density than the physical interactions alone. This explains, for example, the relatively low selectivities observed with the two ketones and phenol (Table II and Figure 2). Hanson
and Van Winkle (40) made a similar observation for 2-butanol with the
binary hexane–hexene 1. As a general rule solvents showing strong
hydrogen bonding affect low selectivities. Another exception to the above
criterion is presented in Figure 8 where *ln S°* for the propylene–propane
pair with six different solvents at 27°C (41) is plotted against τ^2. Decreasing selectivity tends to occur with increasing solvent polar cohesive
energy density. In the same figure the data on pentane–pentene (12)
with the same solvents are also plotted. Here a clear trend of increasing
selectivity with increasing solvent polar cohesive energy density is ob-

served. Because of the similarity between the two hydrocarbon pairs and because the data on the C_5 pair are supported by further experimental evidence (*39*), the C_3 data are of questionable accuracy.

The predictive techniques are rather accurate. However, significant errors have been observed in few cases (*4, 13, 27, 40*). No direct comparison between the three predictive methods is available. The authors of the parachor method (*27*) claim that their method yields equal or better results than the PDD method for the cases considered in their study; it is believed (*42*), however, that the latter is more reliable and it is recommended. The Weimer–Prausnitz method probably gives less accuracy than the PDD method, but it is more general. For example, Hanson and Van Winkle (*40*) report that their data on the hexane–hexene pair were not successfully correlated by the WP method. The Helpinstill–Van Winkle modification is recommended over the WP method. Recently, Null and Palmer (*43*) have presented a modification of the WP method which provides better accuracy but it is less general. The PDD method should be used cautiously when extrapolation with respect to temperature is used (*27*). When the GLC method is used, reliable results are expected. Evaluation of infinite dilution relative volatilities is recommended (*36*).

Literature Cited

1. Berg, L., *Chem. Eng. Progr.* (1969) **65**, 9, 52.
2. Van Winkle, M., "Distillation," p. 436, McGraw–Hill, New York, 1968.
3. Scheibel, E. G., *Chem. Eng. Progr.* (1948) **44**, 927.
4. Pierotti, G. I., Deal, C. H., Derr, E. L., *Ind. Eng. Chem.* (1955) **51**, 95.
5. Tassios, D. P., Van Winkle, M., *J. Chem. Eng. Data* (1967) **12**, 555.
6. Wehe, A. H., Coates, J., *A.I.Ch.E. J.* (1955) **2**, 241.
7. Orye, R. V., Prausnitz, J., *Ind. Eng. Chem.* (1965) **57**, 96.
8. Oliver, E. D., "Diffusional Separation Processes: Theory, Design and Evaluation," p. 189, Wiley, New York, 1966.
9. Prausnitz, J. M., Anderson, R., *A.I.Ch.E. J.* (1961) **7**, 96.
10. Weimer, R. F., Prausnitz, J., *Petrol. Refiner* (1965) **44**, 9, 237.
11. Tassios, D. P., *Chem. Eng.* (1969) **76**, 3, 118.
12. Gerster, J. A., Gordon, J., Eklund, R. B., *J. Chem. Eng. Data* (1960) **5**, 423.
13. Pierotti, G. I., Deal, C. H., Derr, E. L., Document No. 5782, American Documentation Institute, Washington, D. C., 1958.
14. Deal, C. H., Derr, E. L., *Ind. Eng. Chem. Process Design Develop.* (1964) **3**, 394.
15. Prausnitz, J. M., "Molecular Thermodynamics of Fluid-Phase Equilibria," p. 63, Prentice-Hall, Englewood Cliffs, 1969.
16. Watanabe, K., *J. Chem. Phys.* (1954) **22**, 1564.
17. Hammet, L. P., "Physical Organic Chemistry," McGraw–Hill, New York, 1940.
18. Murti, P. S., Van Winkle, M., *A.I.Ch.E. J.* (1957) **3**, 517.
19. Prabhu, P. S., Van Winkle, M., *J. Chem. Eng. Data* (1963) **8**, 14, 210.
20. Stephenson, R. W., Van Winkle, M., *J. Chem. Eng. Data* (1962) **7**, 510.
21. Hess, H. V., *et al.*, "Phase Equilibrium," *Amer. Inst. Chem. Engrs. Symp. Ser.* 2 (1962) 72–79.

22. Gerster, J. A., Mertes, T. S., Colburn, A. P., *Ind. Eng. Chem.* (1947) **39,** 797.
23. Quozati, A., Van Winkle, M., *J. Chem. Eng. Data* (1960) **5,** 269.
24. Jordan, D., Gerster, J. A., Colburn, A. P., Nohl, K., *Chem. Eng. Progr.* (1950) **46,** 601.
25. Baumgarten, P. K., Gerster, J. A., *Ind. Eng. Chem.* (1964) **46,** 2396.
26. Mertes, T. S., Colburn, A. P., *Ind. Eng. Chem.* (1947) **39,** 787.
27. Balakrishnan, S., Krishnan, V., International Symp. on Distillation (1969), p. 49, Inst. Chem. Eng., Brighton, England.
28. Helpinstill, J. G., Van Winkle, M., *Ind. Eng. Chem. Process Design Develop.* (1968) **7,** 213.
29. Wilson, G. M., Deal, C. H., *Ind. Eng. Chem. Fundamentals* (1962) **1,** 20.
30. Deal, C. H., Derr, E. L., Papadopoulos, M. N., *Ind. Eng. Chem. Fundamentals* (1962) **1,** 17.
31. Erdos, E., *Collection Czech. Chem. Commun.* (1956) **21,** 1521.
32. Quale, O. R., *Chem. Rev.* (1953) **53,** 439.
33. Reid, R. C., Sherwood, T. K., "The Properties of Gases and Liquids," p. 373, McGraw–Hill, New York, 1966.
34. Hildebrand, T. H., "Solubility of Non-Electrolyles," p. 131, Dover, New York, 1964.
35. Tassios, D. P., *Hydrocarbon Process. Petrol. Refiner* (1970) **49,** 7, 114.
36. Tassios, D. P., *Ind. Eng. Chem. Process Design Develop.* (1972) **11,** 43.
37. Warren, G. W., Warren, R. R., Yarborough, V. A., *Ind. Eng. Chem.* (1959) **51,** 1475.
38. Sheets, M. R., Marchello, J. M., *Petrol. Refiner* (1963) **42,** 99.
39. Doring, C., *Z. Chem.* (1961) **1,** 347.
40. Hanson, D. O., Van Winkle, M., *J. Chem. Eng. Data* (1967) **12,** 319.
41. Hafslund, E. R., *Chem. Eng. Progr.* (1969) **65,** 9.
42. Prausnitz, J. M., private communication, 1970.
43. Null, H. R., Palmer, D. A., *Chem. Eng. Progr.* (1969) **65,** 9, 47.

RECEIVED November 24, 1970.

5

Azeotropic Distillation Results from Automatic Computer Calculations

CLINE BLACK, R. A. GOLDING, and D. E. DITSLER

Shell Development Co., Emeryville, Calif. 94608

In azeotropic distillation the added component, or entrainer, is taken overhead with one of two or more components being separated in a distillation column. If a second liquid phase forms upon condensing the overhead vapors, the entrainer-rich phase is refluxed or recycled back to the column. The other liquid phase is discarded, recycled to some suitable point in the plant, or processed further to recover dissolved components before being discarded. Methods presented earlier by one of the authors are applied to calculate two and three phase equilibria required in a computer program for calculating azeotropic distillations. A brief description of the program is given; a sample output is listed and described. Calculated results for dehydrating aqueous ethanol mixtures are compared for the entrainers, n-pentane, benzene, and diethyl ether. Column flows, heat loads, and stage requirements are lowest for n-pentane. The entrainers are rated in decreasing order of suitability: n-pentane, benzene, and diethyl ether.

Distribution of components between separable phases is the basis for most commonly used separation methods. Regardless of the type of separation step, its design depends on accurate distribution coefficients for the components between the contacting phases. These are given in compositions or more fundamental properties of the equilibrium phases.

In distillation the components are distributed between separable vapor and liquid phases. The distribution coefficients or K values are the ratios of the vapor–liquid compositions in the equilibrium phases. They are expressed as the liquid phase activity coefficients, γ_i's, the vapor pressures of the pure components $P_i{}^\circ$'s, the total pressure P, and the imperfection-pressure coefficients θ_i's, as

$$K_i = Y_i/x_i = \gamma_i P_i{}^\circ / P\theta_i \tag{1}$$

The relative distribution of components i and j is

$$\alpha_{ij} = K_i/K_j = \gamma_i P_i{}^\circ \theta_j / \gamma_j P_j{}^\circ \theta_i \tag{2}$$

Azeotropic distillation is accomplished by adding to the liquid phase a volatile third component which changes the volatility of one of the two components more than the other, so the components are separated by distillation. The two components to be separated often are close boiling components which do or do not azeotrope in the binary mixture, but sometimes they are components which do azeotrope although they are not close boiling components.

The added third component, sometimes called the entrainer, may form a ternary azeotrope with the two components being separated. However, it must be sufficiently volatile from the solution so that it is taken overhead with one of the two components in the distillation. If the entrainer and the component taken overhead separate into two liquid phases when the vapor overhead is condensed, the entrainer phase is refluxed back to the column. The other phase can be fractionated to remove the dissolved entrainer and the residual amount of the other component before it is discarded. Alternatively, this second liquid phase is recycled to some appropriate place in the main process scheme.

Azeotropic distillation has often been discussed in recent literature (*1, 2, 3*). Methods for providing phase equilibria for azeotropic and extractive distillation have been studied extensively (*1, 4, 5, 6, 7, 8, 9*). Some have discussed the design (*10*) or calculation of azeotropic distillations (*2, 3*); others only discussed choosing the entrainer for azeotropic distillation processes (*11*).

An understanding of the phase equilibria involved is also vital in choosing the entrainer. This not only depends on knowing the pure component vapor pressures but also knowing nonidealities of the components in the liquid and vapor phases.

The methods used here to give the phase equilibria are reviewed, and the Azeotropic Distillation Program ADP/ADPLLE is described. Application of the program to calculate an azeotropic distillation problem is shown and discussed, and a sample computer output is given and is briefly discussed. Finally, calculated azeotropic distillation results are compared for dehydrating aqueous ethanol for the three entrainers, *n*-pentane, benzene, and diethyl ether.

Phase Equilibria

To calculate phase equilibria suitable for most azeotropic distillation problems, the methods should be applicable to three-phase equilibria. Vapor–liquid and liquid–liquid equilibria are usually required. A suitable method for this purpose has already been discussed (5). It is applied here to calculate completely all phase equilibria involved in the usual azeotropic distillation process.

From Equations 1 and 2, the phase equilibria depend upon knowing the pure component vapor pressures $P_i{}^\circ$, liquid phase activity coefficients γ_i and imperfection-pressure coefficients θ_i. The computer program which has been developed uses any of four different vapor pressure equations for providing $P_i{}^\circ$. It uses the modified van Laar Equations (5) to give liquid phase activity coefficients and a Modified van der Waals Equation of State (4, 6) to give imperfection-pressure coefficients θ_i.

The Modified van Laar Equations can represent vapor–liquid and liquid–liquid equilibria. Accordingly, they can be used to predict three-phase equilibria when conditions allow two liquid phases as well as a vapor phase to exist. This might occur on the trays in the distillation column or at the condenser and accumulator for the overhead product from the azeotropic distillation column.

For equilibrium between phases the fugacities for each component must be equal in the several phases. If the fugacity coefficient ϕ_i for any component i in a mixture is defined as the ratio of the fugacity f_i over the vapor composition Y_i and the total pressure P, then

$$\phi_i = f_i^{\,v}/Y_i P \tag{3}$$

If V_i^1 is the liquid molar volume of pure component i and $\overline{V}_i^{\,1}$ is the partial molar volume of component i in the liquid mixture, equilibrium between the liquid and vapor phases is given as

$$\gamma_i^* x_i P_i{}^\circ / \theta_i = Y_i P \tag{4}$$

and

$$\log \theta_i = \log \frac{\phi_i}{\phi_i{}^\circ} - \int_{P^*}^{P_i{}^\circ} \left(\frac{\overline{V}_i^{\,1} - V_i^1}{2.3 RT} \right) dP - \int_{P_i{}^\circ}^{P} \frac{\overline{V}_i^{\,1}}{2.3 RT} \, dP \tag{5}$$

where P^* is the reference pressure.

For most azeotropic distillation problems, the reference pressure is taken equal to the saturation pressure; accordingly, the second term on the right hand side of Equation 5 disappears, to simplify the equation to

$$\log \theta_i = \log \frac{\phi_i}{\phi_i{}^\circ} - \int_{P_i{}^\circ}^{P} \frac{\overline{V}_i^{\,1}}{2.3 RT} \, dP \tag{6}$$

The fugacity coefficients are calculated using a simplified equation of state described earlier $(4, 6)$. For this treatment the constants b_i and a_i are calculated by knowing the critical temperature and pressure. The attraction coefficient ξ_i° is given by generalized coefficients for nonpolar substances and with two other individual constants for polar substances. If Y_i refers to the vapor composition and δ_{ij} refers to binary vapor interactions, the equation becomes

$$\log \phi_i = (P/2.3RT)\,[b_i - a_i\xi_i^\circ/RT] + (P/2.3R^2T^2)\,[(\Sigma G_{ij}Y_j)^2 - (\Sigma \overline{G}_{ij}Y_j)^2] + (P/2.3R^2T^2)\,[\Sigma\delta_{ij}Y_j(1 - Y_i) - 0.5\Sigma_{jk}\delta_{jk}Y_jY_k] \tag{7}$$

When the δ's are zero, the fugacity coefficients in the mixtures are calculated using the simple combination rules for combining the coefficients $(4, 6)$. By using binary interactions, the equations are flexible enough to handle almost any case, even if semi-chemical interactions occur in the vapor phase $(4, 6)$.

In azeotropic distillation, the entrainer and the two components being separated can produce under some conditions three-phase equilibria. Two liquid phases may be in equilibrium with a vapor phase. For the three-phase equilibria the solubility of the nonpolar substance in the polar phase is denoted by x, the solubility of the polar substance in the nonpolar phase by y, and the corresponding activity coefficients by γ and Γ, respectively. The relative volatility for components i and j is related to the total composition X_i according to

$$\alpha_{ij} = \left(\frac{\gamma_i\Gamma_i}{\gamma_j\Gamma_j}\right)\left[\frac{(y_i - X_i)\Gamma_j + (X_i - x_i)\gamma_j}{(y_i - X_i)\Gamma_i + (X_i - x_i)\gamma_i}\right]\left(\frac{P_i^\circ\theta_j}{P_j^\circ\theta_i}\right) \tag{8}$$

Over the two-liquid phase region Equation 8 gives relative volatilities for three-phase equilibria (5). In the composition range where only a polar liquid phase and a vapor phase exists, Equation 8 reduces to

$$\alpha_{ij} = \gamma_i P_i^\circ\theta_j / \gamma_j P_j^\circ\theta_i \tag{9}$$

and where only a nonpolar liquid phase is in equilibrium with a vapor phase, Equation 8 becomes

$$\alpha_{ij} = \Gamma_i P_i^\circ\theta_j / \Gamma_j P_j^\circ\theta_i \tag{10}$$

The isothermal liquid–liquid equilibria are predicted from the Modified van Laar Equations by finding the compositions for which the activities are equal in the two phases for each individual component. This is accomplished with a subprogram called SOLTER.

Either isothermal or isobaric vapor–liquid equilibria or both are calculated with a subprogram called VLE. For SOLTER and VLE, Modified van Laar coefficients for two or three temperatures give the data by which liquid phase activity coefficients are calculated for both programs. For the vapor–liquid equilibria, vapor pressures of the pure components are calculated by one of four different vapor pressure equations. The imperfection-pressure coefficients θ are calculated according to Equations 6 and 7, assuming δ's equal to zero. Approximate values for the partial molar volumes of the liquid are obtained from Equation 4 given in Reference (6).

Azeotropic Distillation Program ADP/ADPLLE

This ternary azeotropic distillation program uses a special system of utility subroutines with programmed initialization. Eight main controls, KNTRL, are used with various options on each. Four parameter options are built into the program, but the values are changed by the user by using PRMTR cards. Twenty-one DATA cards allow the user to give the pertinent conditions and specifications for the separation to be calculated.

A preliminary printout, which prefaces the calculation, defines the controls KNTRL, the parameters PRMTR which are available, and the DATA which must be supplied. This is followed by a maximum of twenty-one V cards which describe quantities which are calculated immediately from the input data. This completes the programmed initialization which describes and defines the controls, the parameters, the data, and certain directly calculatable quantities.

A printout then follows, giving the controls and parameters which have been set and the data which have been supplied by the user on cards. An option provides for printing out the data, for calculating phase equilibria and enthalpies, or for suppressing these. Some calculated results as V quantities are printed out next, and this is followed by a stage-by-stage printout of material flows, heat flows, and detailed phase equilibrium quantities, $P_i°/\theta_i$, x_i, Y_i, α, γ, θ_i. The last printout for the most rigorous calculations gives the compositions of the two liquid phases from the overhead condenser and accumulator and the fraction of the condensed overhead which separates as an aqueous phase.

The program is operated in three general ways. Simplified calculations are made with the subprogram ADP, which calculates the azeotropic distillation column but does not calculate the liquid–liquid equilibria in the accumulator when the overhead vapors are condensed. However, it does try *via* a diagnostic message to warn the user when two liquid phases are expected on the trays. The calculations are rigorous and reliable only when a single liquid phase exists. However, the subprogram ADP does not make reliable calculations when a second liquid phase appears. This program is used for orientation in establishing operating conditions for a design.

The second way in which the program is operated is to calculate rigorously with the subprogram ADPLLE. These calculations are reliable for either two- or three-phase equilibria. The azeotropic distillation columns and the liquid–liquid equilibria for the condensed overhead in the accumulator is calculated with this program.

The third way that the computer program is operated is to use the automated feature. This involves combining calculations *via* ADP and ADPLLE. Starting from a set of operating conditions, which might have been found by using ADP earlier, the program proceeds automatically to find a better set of conditions. The program proceeds with ADP, and after the conditions are established, a final calculation is made *via* ADPLLE.

In these calculations the program tries to adjust conditions so that only a single liquid phase exists on all of the trays in the column. The program first finds the feed tray location at a point where the ratio of components 2 and 3 is the same as the feed when calculated with the initial operating conditions. The feed tray is automatically displaced upward. Then the program determines the lowest water content obtainable in the ethanol product if all other conditions except this and the number of stripping trays are held constant. Using conditions approaching this limit, a final calculation is made with ADPLLE. Usually when it is completed, the top tray is near saturation, and only a single liquid phase exists on the other trays.

Final calculations are made, varying the specification for component 2 in the overhead until the condition is found where the water balance is satisfied when the entire aqueous phase is removed. As the calculation proceeds in steps of one full tray, often a fractional tray is needed to satisfy this exactly, but the nearest full tray to satisfying the value is an acceptable calculation.

A user's manual is not required with this program; the program is submitted without any data, and the user obtains as output a description of the program's features. This prefaces the regular output. It includes a title and identification, a description of control options KNTRL, identification of parameters PRMTR, identification of data DATA, and a description of directly calculatable results, V quantities.

On a first run all options must be set; these are carried forward as set or as reset by the user. The run output shows a control option paragraph only when options are reset and only those that are reset.

Parameters are built in and remain fixed unless changed by parameter cards. The parameter paragraph appears only on runs where resetting occurs and only on those that are reset.

Data values are loaded for all data on a first run; these are carried forward until they are reset. The data pragraph appears on all runs for which at least one value was reset and shows all values whether reset or not.

Basic data decks for phase equilibria and enthalpies are included in the program itself for twenty different ternaries as shown in KNTRL 2, options 1–20. For other systems the data are loaded as indicated, KNTRL 2, option 21.

The Lewis and Matheson technique makes tray-to-tray calculations starting at the bottom and calculating up the column. Material and heat balances are made on each tray, the number of trays is determined in the calculations.

Application

A sample calculation is given showing the use of the program to calculate the azeotropic distillation of aqueous ethanol mixtures using the entrainer n-pentane (KNTRL 2, Option 7).

The feed to the column is 242.02 moles/hr of aqueous ethanol at a temperature of 110°F. The feed composition is 85.64 mole % ethanol. The distillation is carried out at 50 psia at the reboiler. The pressure drop is assumed to be 0.14 psi per tray. The vapor boil-up at the reboiler is set at 800 moles/hr. The reflux temperature is 154.45°F. The aqueous phase is stripped to remove dissolved entrainer and residual ethanol. The calculation control is set to reduce ethanol in the overhead vapors to 13.85 mole %.

Another specification which is set at the beginning is the mole fraction of entrainer which will be allowed in the bottom product, ethanol; this has been set at 0.62×10^{-6}. A starting and maximum allowable value for the fraction of water in the final bottom product is set at 2.556×10^{-4}. If the program fails on the first ADP cycle in the automated calculation, the vapor boil-up is increased.

If a stripper is used to remove entrainer and residual ethanol from the aqueous phase, the data input on DATA cards 13, 14 and 15 must be appropriately specified. These data cards give the mole fractions of entrainer, ethanol, and water, respectively, in the stripper bottoms referred to as DISTILLATE. If no stripper is included, the data of cards 13, 14 and 15 correspond to the composition of the aqueous phase being removed. Here the input is only a first approximation, and the program will calculate a new value in the second cycle, the number of which must be specified or the tolerance given if no stripper is included.

Although the rigorous stripper calculation is made separately, a fairly realistic bottom product is assumed when the stripper is included. For this calculation a trace of pentane 1×10^{-5} and a small fraction of ethanol 9×10^{-5} have been assumed in the stripper bottoms. The accumulator temperature is assumed the same as the reflux, 154.45°F. For this sample calculation no values are specified on DATA cards 7, 12, 18, 19, 20, and 21 since the program does not use these for this calculation, but the DATA cards should be included in the input deck.

The sample calculation is shown as Table I. The first four pages describe the features of the program. The first page of the computer output shows control options KNTRL 1–8; the three ways in which the program is used are defined as options 1, 2, and 3 for KNTRL 1. Data for twenty different ternary systems involving an entrainer and two components being separated are included in the program; these constitute options 1–20 of KNTROL 2. Option 21 is used when all data for a new system are used and are loaded as input. The two options 1 and 2 of KNTRL 3 determine when the calculations are completed. The options 1 and 2 of KNTRL 4 determines the feed tray location; the KNTRL's 5–8 allow the user to choose reasonable run conditions and output.

The second page of computer output shows the options for parameters which are written into the program but can be changed by parameter cards P1–P4. The third page of computer output shows the data input as D1–D21 which the user supplies in making a run. The fourth page of output shows the twenty-one V quantities which are calculated in the program from the input. The fifth page summarizes the options selected and the data introduced as input for the sample problem. The thermodynamic data are given on computer output page 6; quantities calculated in the program from the input data are summarized as V quantities on output page 7. Shown on output pages 8 and 9 is the final ADP run in the automated calculation; these provide input to the ADPI,LE run. The V quantities are summarized on output page 10, and the final stage-to-stage results appear on output pages 11–15.

These last five pages of computer output provide a tray-to-tray summary of heat and material flows and detailed quantities for the phase equilibria, also a summary of the three-phase condenser and accumulator results and the water product out. The last output page shows the fraction of the aqueous phase that satisfies the water balance. Since only full stages are calculated, this fraction normally is not exactly unity, but it should reprsent the nearest full stage result to satisfy the water balance. The entrainer makeup and the water product out is shown last in the computer printout.

From the computer results column profiles have been summarized and are given in Table II. The pressure profile is linear with tray number resulting from the assumed input data for pressure drop per tray. Also in the table is the temperature, the fraction of pentane in the liquid phase, the fraction of water in the vapor phase on a pentane-free basis, and the fraction of ethanol in the liquid phase for each tray in the column.

Table I.　Ternary Azeotropic Distillation Program　(ADP/ADPLLE)

```
TERNARY AZEOTROPIC DISTILLATION PROGRAM (ADP/ADPLLE)

THIS PROGRAM USES A SPECIAL SYSTEM OF UTILITY SUBROUTINES, WITH PROGRAMMED INITIALIZATION AS FOLLOWS      Computer Output Page 1


THESE CONTROL OPTIONS ARE AVAILABLE.


KNTRL ( 1) =  1        ADP PROGRAM
KNTRL ( 1) =  2        ADPLLE PROGRAM
KNTRL ( 1) =  3        COMBINATION OF ADP/ADPLLE PROGRAMS

KNTRL ( 2) =  1        SYSTEM  1
KNTRL ( 2) =  2        SYSTEM  2
KNTRL ( 2) =  3        SYSTEM  3
KNTRL ( 2) =  4        SYSTEM  4
KNTRL ( 2) =  5        SYSTEM  5
KNTRL ( 2) =  6        SYSTEM  6
KNTRL ( 2) =  7        SYSTEM  7    PNTAN2-ETHNOL-WATER
KNTRL ( 2) =  8        SYSTEM  8
KNTRL ( 2) =  9        SYSTEM  9
KNTRL ( 2) = 10
KNTRL ( 2) = 11        SYSTEM 11
KNTRL ( 2) = 12        SYSTEM 12
KNTRL ( 2) = 13        SYSTEM 13
KNTRL ( 2) = 14        SYSTEM 14
KNTRL ( 2) = 15        SYSTEM 15
KNTRL ( 2) = 16        SYSTEM 16
KNTRL ( 2) = 17        SYSTEM 17
KNTRL ( 2) = 18        SYSTEM 18
KNTRL ( 2) = 19
KNTRL ( 2) = 20
KNTRL ( 2) = 21        LOAD ALL COMPONENT DATA FROM CARDS AFTER UTILITY DATA

KNTRL ( 3) =  1        SET COMP(2) CONTENT IN TOPS VAPOR
KNTRL ( 3) =  2        SET COMP(3) CONTENT IN REFLUX

KNTRL ( 4) =  1        SET FEED TRAY AT SAME COMP(2)/COMP(3) RATIO AS FEED
KNTRL ( 4) =  2        SET FEED TRAY BY DATA CARD INPUT  (D(12))

KNTRL ( 5) =  1        ACCUMULATOR CALCULATION ISOTHERMAL    (IF KNTRL(1)=2,3)
KNTRL ( 5) =  2        ACCUMULATOR CALCULATION ISOBARIC      (IF KNTRL(1)=2,3)
KNTRL ( 5) =  3        ACCUMULATOR NOT CALCULATED

KNTRL ( 6) =  1        HEATER/SUBCOOLER PRESENT              (IF KNTRL(5)=1,2)
KNTRL ( 6) =  2        HEATER/SUBCOOLER NOT PRESENT

KNTRL ( 7) =  1        STRIPPER NOT PRESENT  (MUST SET D(20) IF KNTRL(1)=2,3)
KNTRL ( 7) =  2        STRIPPER NOT PRESENT  (MUST SET D(21) IF KNTRL(1)=2,3)
KNTRL ( 7) =  3        STRIPPER PRESENT (PROGRAM CYCLES ONCE IF KNTRL(1)=2,3)
```

```
KNTRL ( 8) = 1        PRINT ALL COMPONENT DATA
KNTRL ( 8) = 2        SUPPRESS PRINTING OF ALL COMPONENT DATA
```

THESE QUANTITIES ARE BUILT INTO THE PROGRAM AS PARAMETERS, BUT THE VALUES MAY BE CHANGED BY THE USER   Computer Output Page 2
      THROUGH THE USE OF PRMTR-CARDS.

```
MAX CYCLES(IF KNTRL(1)=2,3 AND KNTRL(7)=1)       P( 1) =        9.0
MAX CYCLES(IF KNTRL(1)=2,3 AND KNTRL(7)=2)       P( 2) =        6.0
FEED TRAY DISPLACEMENT(ONLY IF KNTRL(1)=3)       P( 3) =        3.0
MAXIMUM ADP PASSES ALLOWED (IF KNTRL(1)=3)       P( 4) =       25.0
```

THESE QUANTITIES ARE TO BE SUPPLIED BY THE USER BY MEANS OF DATA-CARDS.   Computer Output Page 3

```
D( 1) = FEED        COMP(2)     MOLES/HR                              FORMAT    E15.8
D( 2) = FEED        COMP(2)     MOLE FRACTION                         FORMAT    E15.8
D( 3) = FEED TEMPERATURE        FAHRENHEIT (SUBCOOLED LIQUID)  FORMAT    E15.8
D( 4) = REBOILER PRESSURE       PSIA                                  FORMAT    E15.8
D( 5) = PRESSURE DROP PER TRAY  PSIA                                  FORMAT    E15.8
D( 6) = REFLUX TEMPERATURE      FAHRENHEIT                            FORMAT    E15.8
D( 7) = REFLUX      COMP(3)     MOLE FRACTION   (IF KNTRL(3)=2) FORMAT    E15.8
D( 8) = REBOILER VAPOR          MOLES/HR                              FORMAT    E15.8
D( 9) = BOTTOMS     COMP(1)     MOLE FRACTION                         FORMAT    E15.8
D(10) = BOTTOMS     COMP(3)     MOLE FRACTION                         FORMAT    E15.8
D(11) = TOPS VAPOR  COMP(2)     MOLE FRACTION   (IF KNTRL(3)=1) FORMAT    E15.8
D(12) = FEED TRAY LOCATION                      (IF KNTRL(4)=2) FORMAT    E15.8
D(13) = DISTILLATE  COMP(1)     MOLE FRACTION                         FORMAT    E15.8
D(14) = DISTILLATE  COMP(2)     MOLE FRACTION                         FORMAT    E15.8
D(15) = DISTILLATE  COMP(3)     MOLE FRACTION                         FORMAT    E15.8
D(16) = FEED        COMP(1)     MOLE FRACTION                         FORMAT    E15.8
D(17) = ACCUMULATOR TEMPERATURE FAHRENHEIT  (DT IF KNTRL(5)=2) FORMAT    E15.8
D(18) = DP (TOP PRESS-AC PRESS) PSIA            (IF KNTRL(5)=2) FORMAT    E15.8
D(19) = HEATER/SUBCOOLER TEMP   FAHRENHEIT      (IF KNTRL(6)=1) FORMAT    E15.8
D(20) = NUMBER OF CYCLES FOR ADPLLE             (IF KNTRL(7)=1) FORMAT    F10.1
D(21) = TOLERANCE OF COMP(2) AND COMP(3)        (IF KNTRL(7)=2) FORMAT    E15.8
```

DESCRIPTIVE IDENTIFICATIONS HAVE BEEN ESTABLISHED FOR THESE VARIABLES.   Computer Output Page 4

```
V( 1) = FEED        COMP(1)     MOLES/HR                              FORMAT    E15.8
V( 2) = FEED        COMP(2)     MOLES/HR                              FORMAT    E15.8
V( 3) = FEED        COMP(3)     MOLES/HR                              FORMAT    E15.8
V( 4) = FEED        TOTAL       MOLES/HR                              FORMAT    E15.8
V( 5) = BOTTOMS     COMP(1)     MOLES/HR                              FORMAT    E15.8
V( 6) = BOTTOMS     COMP(2)     MOLES/HR                              FORMAT    E15.8
V( 7) = BOTTOMS     COMP(3)     MOLES/HR                              FORMAT    E15.8
V( 8) = BOTTOMS     TOTAL       MOLES/HR                              FORMAT    E15.8
V( 9) = DISTILLATE  COMP(1)     MOLES/HR                              FORMAT    E15.8
V(10) = DISTILLATE  COMP(2)     MOLES/HR                              FORMAT    E15.8
```

```
V(11) = DISTILLATE  COMP(3)       MOLES/HR                            FORMAT  E15.8
V(12) = DISTILLATE  TOTAL         MOLES/HR                            FORMAT  E15.8
V(13) = COMP(1) VAPOR-LIQUID FLOW STRIPPING SECTION     MOLES/HR FORMAT  E15.8
V(14) = COMP(2) VAPOR-LIQUID FLOW STRIPPING SECTION     MOLES/HR FORMAT  E15.8
V(15) = COMP(3) VAPOR-LIQUID FLOW STRIPPING SECTION     MOLES/HR FORMAT  E15.8
V(16) =                 HEAT FLOW STRIPPING SECTION      BTU/HR FORMAT  E15.8
V(17) = COMP(1) VAPOR-LIQUID FLOW RECTIFYING SECTION    MOLES/HR FORMAT  E15.8
V(18) = COMP(2) VAPOR-LIQUID FLOW RECTIFYING SECTION    MOLES/HR FORMAT  E15.8
V(19) = COMP(3) VAPOR-LIQUID FLOW RECTIFYING SECTION    MOLES/HR FORMAT  E15.8
V(20) =                 HEAT FLOW RECTIFYING SECTION     BTU/HR FORMAT  E15.8
V(21) =                 VALUE OF D(10) WHEN KNTRL(1)=3          FORMAT  E15.8


                TERNARY AZEOTROPIC DISTILLATION PROGRAM (ADP/ADPLLE)

RUN NO  99              TEST OF ADP/ADPLLE OPTION KNTRL(1)=3


THE CONTROL OPTIONS HAVE BEEN SET AS FOLLOWS

KNTRL ( 1) = 3          COMBINATION OF ADP/ADPLLE PROGRAMS
KNTRL ( 2) = 7          SYSTEM  7   PNTAN2-ETHNOL-WATER
KNTRL ( 3) = 1          SET COMP(2) CONTENT IN TOPS VAPOR
KNTRL ( 4) = 1          SET FEED TRAY AT SAME COMP(2)/COMP(3) RATIO AS FEED
KNTRL ( 5) = 1          ACCUMULATOR CALCULATION ISOTHERMAL   (IF KNTRL(1)=2,3)
KNTRL ( 6) = 2          HEATER/SUBCOOLER NOT PRESENT
KNTRL ( 7) = 3          STRIPPER PRESENT (PROGRAM CYCLES ONCE IF KNTRL(1)=2,3)
KNTRL ( 8) = 1          PRINT ALL COMPONENT DATA


THE FOLLOWING DATA ARE USED FOR THIS CALCULATION

FEED        COMP(2)     MOLES/HR                         D( 1) =  .24202000+03
FEED        COMP(2)     MOLE FRACTION                    D( 2) =  .85640000-00
FEED TEMPERATURE        FAHRENHEIT  (SUBCOOLED LIQUID)   D( 3) =  .11000000+03
REBOILER PRESSURE       PSIA                             D( 4) =  .50000000+02
PRESSURE DROP PER TRAY  PSIA                             D( 5) =  .14000000-00
REFLUX TEMPERATURE      FAHRENHEIT                       D( 6) =  .15445000+03
REFLUX      COMP(3)     MOLE FRACTION  (IF KNTRL(3)=2)   D( 7) =  .34999999-01
REBOILER VAPOR          MOLES/HR                         D( 8) =  .80000000+03
BOTTOMS     COMP(1)     MOLE FRACTION                    D( 9) =  .61999999-06
BOTTOMS     COMP(3)     MOLE FRACTION                    D(10) =  .25560000-03
TOPS VAPOR  COMP(2)     MOLE FRACTION  (IF KNTRL(3)=1)   D(11) =  .13850000-00
FEED TRAY LOCATION                     (IF KNTRL(4)=2)   D(12) =  .15000000+02
DISTILLATE  COMP(1)     MOLE FRACTION                    D(13) =  .99999999-05
DISTILLATE  COMP(2)     MOLE FRACTION                    D(14) =  .89999999-04
DISTILLATE  COMP(3)     MOLE FRACTION                    D(15) =  .99990000-00
FEED        COMP(1)     MOLE FRACTION                    D(16) =  .00000000
ACCUMULATOR TEMPERATURE FAHRENHEIT  (DT IF KNTRL(5)=2)   D(17) =  .15445000+03
DP (TOP PRESS-AC PRESS) PSIA          (IF KNTRL(5)=2)    D(18) =  .00000000
HEATER/SUBCOOLER TEMP   FAHRENHEIT    (IF KNTRL(6)=1)    D(19) =  .00000000
NUMBER OF CYCLES FOR ADPLLE           (IF KNTRL(7)=1)    D(20) =      .0
TOLERANCE OF COMP(2) AND COMP(3)      (IF KNTRL(7)=2)    D(21) =  .00000000
```

AZEOTROPIC DISTILLATION PROGRAM (ADP/ADPLLE)

MODIFICATION OF PROGRAM TO CALCULATE PHASE EQUILIBRIA BY PROCEDURES AND
COEFFICIENTS USED IN 'VLE' PROGRAM.   USES MODIFIED VAN LAAR COEFFICIENTS
AT 3 TEMPS.   CALCULATES THETAS, GAMMAS AND COMPLETE PHASE EQUILIBRIA AT
EACH STAGE.

ISOTHERMAL ACCUMULATOR CALCULATION

TEMP = 154.450 F

HEATER/SUBCOOLER NOT PRESENT
STRIPPER PRESENT

RUN CYCLES = 1

AIJ	AJI	CIJ	TEMP	I J
.93892520-00	.92929000-00	.17486500-00	75.000 C	PNTAN2-ETHNOL
.41365440+01	.24165000+01	.29700000-00	75.000 C	PNTAN2-WATER
.72799999-00	.40700000-00	.00000000	75.000 C	ETHNOL-WATER

AIJ	AJI	CIJ	TEMP	I J
.88388000-00	.87359000-00	.15507500-00	87.800 C	PNTAN2-ETHNOL
.39480000+01	.22125185+01	.25800000-00	87.800 C	PNTAN2-WATER
.74600000-00	.40080000-00	.00000000	87.800 C	ETHNOL-WATER

AIJ	AJI	CIJ	TEMP	I J
.83367725-00	.82406500-00	.13747500-00	100.000 C	PNTAN2-ETHNOL
.37712938+01	.20300000+01	.22500000-00	100.000 C	PNTAN2-WATER
.76050000-00	.39250000-00	.00000000	100.000 C	ETHNOL-WATER

2 CLASSES   1   2

-- COEFFICIENTS FOR VAPOR PRESSURE EQUATIONS ---------------------------------

PNTAN2	.226933+02	.208645+04	.273160+03	.525170+01	.159785+01	.0000
ETHNOL	.816290+01	.162322+04	.228980+03	.000000	.000000	.0000
WATER	.208440+02	.281740+04	.273160+03	.404859+01	.000000	.0000

	TC K	PC ATMS	CHI CC/GM	EPR	AMPR
PNTAN2	.470300+03	.331000+02	.141000+03	.000000	.000000
ETHNOL	.516300+03	.631000+02	.759000+02	.890000-01	.475000+01
WATER	.647000+03	.218000+03	.247000+02	.260000-01	.475000+01

	TEMP F	LIQ BTU/MOL	VAP BTU/MOL
PNTAN2	100.000	.39682500+04	.15151500+05
PNTAN2	200.000	.82972500+04	.17748900+05
PNTAN2	300.000	.13275600+05	.20346300+05
ETHNOL	100.000	.25061000+04	.20937900+05
ETHNOL	200.000	.60349000+04	.22573300+05
ETHNOL	300.000	.10365300+05	.23969200+05
WATER	100.000	.12250000+04	.19916000+05
WATER	200.000	.30270000+04	.20649000+05
WATER	300.000	.48200000+04	.21290001+05

```
       --- LIQUID --------- ENTHALPY EQUATION COEFFICIENTS --------- VAPOR ---
PNTAN2   .288600+03   .335498+02   .324675-01   .125541+05   .259740+02   .372529-08
ETHNOL -.221100+03   .232640+02   .400800-01   .190630+05   .199465+02 -.119750-01
WATER  -.566000+03   .181550+02 -.450000-03   .190910+05   .871000+01 -.460000-02
```

PRELIMINARY RESULTS FOLLOW

PROGRAM HAS CALCULATED THE FOLLOWING VARIABLES

```
FEED         COMP(1)    MOLES/HR              V( 1) =  .00000000
FEED         COMP(2)    MOLES/HR              V( 2) =  .24202000+03
FEED         COMP(3)    MOLES/HR              V( 3) =  .40581588+02
FEED         TOTAL      MOLES/HR              V( 4) =  .28260159+03
BOTTOMS      COMP(1)    MOLES/HR              V( 5) =  .15005057-03
BOTTOMS      COMP(2)    MOLES/HR              V( 6) =  .24201635+03
BOTTOMS      COMP(3)    MOLES/HR              V( 7) =  .56181042-03
BOTTOMS      TOTAL      MOLES/HR              V( 8) =  .24201705+03
DISTILLATE   COMP(1)    MOLES/HR              V( 9) =  .40584534-03
DISTILLATE   COMP(2)    MOLES/HR              V(10) =  .36526080-02
DISTILLATE   COMP(3)    MOLES/HR              V(11) =  .40580475+02
DISTILLATE   TOTAL      MOLES/HR              V(12) =  .40584534+02
             VALUE OF D(10) WHEN KNTPL(1)=3   V(21) =  .23213671-05
```

Computer Output Page 7

Computer Output Page 8

```
REBOILER   PRESSURE=  50.000   TEMP= 234.910
COMP       VAPOR M/HR   LIQ M/HR   LIQ BTU/M   VAP BTU/M   VP/THETA   X (01)     Y        ALPHA      GAMMA     THETA
PNTAN2        .0059        .0061   9961.3993  18655.6430   98.3158   .000006   .000007  11.947562  6.076075  1.146542
ETHNOL     799.9920    1042.0083   7455.5545  23087.8140   49.9997   .999992   .999990   1.000000  1.000000   .999999
WATER         .0021        .0026   3653.9526  20883.2230   23.1712   .000003   .000003   1.116915  2.410122   .983621
TOTAL      800.0000    1042.0170   7768820.1  18470220.0
MOLE FRACTION WATER (ENTRAINER FREE BASIS)                           .000003   .000003

KTRAY= 1   PRESSURE=  49.860   TEMP= 234.748   M= 2   N= 5   KNTRL(10)= 0
COMP       VAPOR M/HR   LIQ M/HR   LIQ BTU/M   VAP BTU/M   VP/THETA   X ( 2)     Y        ALPHA      GAMMA     THETA
PNTAN2        .0558        .0559   9944.2387  18651.4540   98.1421   .000054   .000070  11.969771  6.080710  1.146420
ETHNOL     799.1022    1041.1186   7440.7544  23085.5050   49.8567   .999944   .999927   1.000000  1.000000   .999994
WATER         .0023        .0028   3647.6417  20882.1670   23.1020   .000003   .000003   1.116991  2.410589   .983646
TOTAL      799.1602    1041.1773   7747273.7  18448765.0
MOLE FRACTION WATER (ENTRAINER FREE BASIS)                           .000003   .000003

KTRAY= 2   PRESSURE=  49.720   TEMP= 234.558   M= 2   N= 6   KNTRL(10)= 0
COMP       VAPOR M/HR   LIQ M/HR   LIQ BTU/M   VAP BTU/M   VP/THETA   X ( 3)     Y        ALPHA      GAMMA     THETA
PNTAN2        .5139        .5141   9921.9861  18646.5080   97.9429   .000494   .000644  11.993293  6.084698  1.146209
ETHNOL     797.7091    1039.7254   7421.5674  23082.7760   49.6905   .999503   .999353   1.000000  1.000000   .999943
WATER         .0024        .0030   3639.4535  20880.9200   23.0212   .000003   .000003   1.117174  2.411380   .983646
TOTAL      798.2254    1040.2425   7721503.4  18422972.0
MOLE FRACTION WATER (ENTRAINER FREE BASIS)                           .000003   .000003
```

```
KTRAY= 3    PRESSURE=  49.580    TEMP= 234.102    M= 2    N= 6    KNTRL(IO)= 0
COMP      VAPOR M/HR    LIQ M/HR    LIQ BTU/M    VAP BTU/M    VP/THETA    X ( 4)        Y        ALPHA       GAMMA       THETA
PNTAN2       4.6852       4.6854    9783.6952   18634.6550    97.5110   .004529    .005912   12.028157    6.082606   1.145188
ETHNOL     787.8411    1029.8574    7302.4418   23076.2360    49.3110   .995468    .994085    1.000000    1.000001    .999483
WATER         .0025        .0031    3588.4516   20877.9290    22.8338   .000003    .000003    1.118356    2.415163    .983429
TOTAL      792.5288    1034.5459    7566325.0   18267766.0             .000003    .000003
MOLE FRACTION WATER (ENTRAINER FREE BASIS)

KTRAY= 4    PRESSURE=  49.440    TEMP= 231.260    M= 3    N= 5    KNTRL(IO)= 0
COMP      VAPOR M/HR    LIQ M/HR    LIQ BTU/M    VAP BTU/M    VP/THETA    X ( 5)        Y        ALPHA       GAMMA       THETA
PNTAN2      39.8050      39.8052    8858.5103   18560.8360    95.0046   .039750    .052418   12.158980    6.023068   1.137047
ETHNOL     719.5733     961.5896    6510.6443   23035.3850    47.0586   .960247    .947579    1.000000    1.000061    .995459
WATER         .0024        .0030    3241.9305   20859.2590    21.7125   .000003    .000003    1.128858    2.446777    .981333
TOTAL      759.3808    1001.3978    6613192.3   17314512.0             .000003    .000003
MOLE FRACTION WATER (ENTRAINER FREE BASIS)

KTRAY= 5    PRESSURE=  49.300    TEMP= 211.961    M= 3    N= 5    KNTRL(IO)= 0
COMP      VAPOR M/HR    LIQ M/HR    LIQ BTU/M    VAP BTU/M    VP/THETA    X ( 6)        Y        ALPHA       GAMMA       THETA
PNTAN2     268.0904     268.0906    7318.0596   18059.5690    78.7405   .260787    .341087   12.505131    5.372543   1.088142
ETHNOL     517.8967     759.9131    5213.8250   22752.8710    33.6685   .739211    .658911    1.000000    1.004769    .971859
WATER         .0020        .0026    2642.8492   20730.5130    15.1609   .000002    .000003    1.233287    2.751869    .969674
TOTAL      785.9892    1028.0062    5923958.0   16625276.4             .000003    .000004
MOLE FRACTION WATER (ENTRAINER FREE BASIS)

KTRAY= 6    PRESSURE=  49.160    TEMP= 178.640    M= 3    N= 5    KNTRL(IO)= 0
COMP      VAPOR M/HR    LIQ M/HR    LIQ BTU/M    VAP BTU/M    VP/THETA    X ( 7)        Y        ALPHA       GAMMA       THETA
PNTAN2     656.3955     656.3956    6894.4591   17194.0960    54.1901   .550284    .690351    6.319559    2.401460   1.018203
ETHNOL     294.4158     536.4321    4862.3906   22244.0940    17.5479   .449714    .309646    1.000000    1.173503    .947050
WATER         .0022        .0028    2472.8385   20500.1590     7.5945   .000002    .000002    2.225791    6.035234    .959809
TOTAL      950.8135    1192.8305    7133842.3   17835185.0             .000005    .000007
MOLE FRACTION WATER (ENTRAINER FREE BASIS)

KTRAY= 7    PRESSURE=  49.020    TEMP= 169.194    M= 3    N= 3    KNTRL(IO)= 0
```

Computer Output Page 9

```
COMP      VAPOR M/HR    LIQ M/HR    LIQ BTU/M    VAP BTU/M    VP/THETA    X ( 8)        Y        ALPHA       GAMMA       THETA
PNTAN2     792.9419     792.9420    6817.9567   16948.7490    48.2035   .631133    .781714    2.926727    1.444628   1.001735
ETHNCL     221.4156     463.4319    4799.1707   22095.0280    14.3011   .368863    .218281    1.000000    1.663730    .944806
WATER         .0050        .0056    2441.8741   20432.9990     6.1290   .000004    .000005    4.415987   17.143145    .959835
TOTAL     1014.3625    1256.3795    7530346.8   18331659.0             .000012    .000023
MOLE FRACTION WATER (ENTRAINER FREE BASIS)

KTRAY= 8    PRESSURE=  48.880    TEMP= 167.474    M= 2    N= 7    KNTRL(IO)= 0
COMP      VAPOR M/HR    LIQ M/HR    LIQ BTU/M    VAP BTU/M    VP/THETA    X ( 9)        Y        ALPHA       GAMMA       THETA
PNTAM2     824.6641     824.6642    6797.2936   16904.0770    47.1540   .649058    .801782    2.364207    1.316887    .998997
ET-NOL     203.8620     445.8793    4782.1087   22067.6550    13.7553   .350932    .198205    1.000000    1.909471    .945259
WATER         .0131        .0137    2433.4969   20420.6820     5.8866   .000011    .000013    5.328614   23.775542    .960357
TOTAL     1028.5392    1270.5562    7737756.5   18439207.0             .000031    .000064
MOLE FRACTION WATER (ENTRAINER FREE BASIS)
```

```
KTRAY= 9    PRESSURE=   48.740    TEMP= 167.009    M= 2    N= 6    KNTRL(10)= 0
  COMP      VAPOR M/HR    LIQ M/HR    LIQ BTU/M    VAP BTU/M    VP/THETA    X (10)        Y        ALPHA       GAMMA       THETA
  PNTAN2     831.2025     831.2026    6786.5001   16891.9910    46.8633    .652849    .806073    2.247757    1.291647    .998512
  ETHNOL     199.9386     441.9550    4773.1986   22060.2390    13.6104    .347124    .193894    1.000000    1.978584    .945469
  WATER         .0341        .0347    2429.1187   20417.3450     5.8227    .000027    .000033    5.563437   25.730409    .960537
  TOTAL     1031.1753    1273.1922   7750579.6   18452055.0
  MOLE FRACTION WATER (ENTRAINER FREE BASIS)                                         .000078    .000171

KTRAY=10    PRESSURE=   48.600    TEMP= 166.766    M= 2    N= 6    KNTRL(10)= 0
  COMP      VAPOR M/HR    LIQ M/HR    LIQ BTU/M    VAP BTU/M    VP/THETA    X (11)        Y        ALPHA       GAMMA       THETA
  PNTAN2     832.4716     832.4717    6777.2436   16885.6750    46.7014    .653727    .807122    2.225964    1.286568    .998423
  ETHNOL     198.8485     440.8649    4765.5584   22056.3600    13.5342    .346204    .192793    1.000000    1.994401    .945570
  WATER         .0877        .0883    2425.3626   20415.6010     5.7891    .000069    .000085    5.621552   26.211532    .960616
  TOTAL     1031.4078    1273.4248   7743044.8   18444509.0
  MOLE FRACTION WATER (ENTRAINER FREE BASIS)                                         .000200    .000441

KTRAY=11    PRESSURE=   48.460    TEMP= 166.557    M= 2    N= 6    KNTRL(10)= 0
  COMP      VAPOR M/HR    LIQ M/HR    LIQ BTU/M    VAP BTU/M    VP/THETA    X (12)        Y        ALPHA       GAMMA       THETA
  PNTAN2     832.5859     832.5860    6767.7421   16880.2570    46.5613    .653979    .807480    2.223730    1.285568    .998405
  ETHNOL     198.2818     440.2982    4757.7173   22053.0310    13.4698    .345845    .192303    1.000000    1.998380    .945640
  WATER         .2240        .2246    2421.5060   20414.1040     5.7606    .000176    .000217    5.642222   26.364322    .960670
  TOTAL     1031.0917    1273.1087   7730085.3   18431551.0
  MOLE FRACTION WATER (ENTRAINER FREE BASIS)                                         .000510    .001128

KTRAY=12    PRESSURE=   48.320    TEMP= 166.343    M= 2    N= 6    KNTRL(10)= 0
  COMP      VAPOR M/HR    LIQ M/HR    LIQ BTU/M    VAP BTU/M    VP/THETA    X (13)        Y        ALPHA       GAMMA       THETA
  PNTAN2     832.2150     832.2152    6756.8310   16874.6930    46.4180    .654003    .807602    2.226203    1.285508    .998385
  ETHNOL     197.6918     439.7081    4748.7144   22049.6130    13.4043    .345548    .191845    1.000000    1.999638    .945688
  WATER         .5703        .5708    2417.0756   20412.5660     5.7317    .000449    .000553    5.655481   26.447168    .960708
  TOTAL     1030.4771    1272.4941   7712565.2   18414041.0
  MOLE FRACTION WATER (ENTRAINER FREE BASIS)                                         .001296    .002876

KTRAY=13    PRESSURE=   48.180    TEMP= 166.097    M= 2    N= 6    KNTRL(10)= 0
  COMP      VAPOR M/HR    LIQ M/HR    LIQ BTU/M    VAP BTU/M    VP/THETA    X (14)        Y        ALPHA       GAMMA       THETA
  PNTAN2     831.1006     831.1008    6742.1831   16868.3020    46.2556    .653721    .807425    2.231599    1.285956    .998324
  ETHNOL     196.7734     438.7897    4736.6308   22045.6850    13.3303    .345140    .191168    1.000000    1.999564    .945688
  WATER        1.4478       1.4483    2411.1252   20410.7990     5.6989    .001139    .001407    5.667623   26.508446    .960717
  TOTAL     1029.3218    1271.3388   7685310.7   18386810.0
  MOLE FRACTION WATER (ENTRAINER FREE BASIS)                                         .003290    .007304

KTRAY=14    PRESSURE=   48.040    TEMP= 165.766    M= 2    N= 7    KNTRL(10)= 0
  COMP      VAPOR M/HR    LIQ M/HR    LIQ BTU/M    VAP BTU/M    VP/THETA    X (15)        Y        ALPHA       GAMMA       THETA
  PNTAN2     828.2288     828.2290    6718.2870   16859.7180    46.0426    .652722    .806559    2.242630    1.287324    .998153
  ETHNOL     194.9825     436.9988    4716.9242   22040.4060    13.2332    .344396    .189881    1.000000    1.997222    .945570
  WATER        3.6558       3.6564    2401.4117   20408.4250     5.6556    .002882    .003560    5.680406   26.545656    .960652

  TOTAL     1026.8671    1268.8842   7634350.7   16335807.0
  MOLE FRACTION WATER (ENTRAINER FREE BASIS)                                         .008298    .018404

KTRAY=15    PRESSURE=   47.900    TEMP= 165.227    M= 3    N= 3    KNTRL(10)= 0
  COMP      VAPOR M/HR    LIQ M/HR    LIQ BTU/M    VAP BTU/M    VP/THETA    X (16)        Y        ALPHA       GAMMA       THETA
  PNTAN2     821.2204     821.2205    6672.9946   16845.7060    45.7047    .649994    .804006    2.267586    1.290944    .997709
```

Computer Output Page 10

```
ETHANOL      191.0846     433.1010    4679.5937   22031.7840      13.0792    .342798    .187079   1.000000    1.989408    .945163
WATER          9.1057       9.1062    2382.9789   20404.5470       5.5864    .007208    .008915   5.695275   26.527143    .960408
TOTAL       1021.4107    1263.4277    7528436.8   18229770.0
MOLE FRACTION WATER (ENTRAINER FREE BASIS)                                   .020593    .045485

NEXT TRAY IS FEED TRAY


KTRAY=16    PRESSURE=   47.760   TEMP= 164.203    M= 3   N= 4    KNTRL(10)= 0
  COMP      VAPOR M/HR     LIQ M/HR    LIQ BTU/M    VAP BTU/M    VP/THETA     X (17)        Y       ALPHA       GAMMA       THETA
  PNTAN2      805.1856     805.1857    6581.6141   16819.1180      45.0731    .643332    .797554   2.327323    1.300168    .996623
  ETHANOL     182.4605     424.4768    4604.3625   22015.4040      12.7925    .339151    .180731   1.000000    1.968362    .944075
  WATER        21.9231      21.9236    2345.7019   20397.1830       5.4569    .017517    .021715   5.714574   26.369356    .959741
  TOTAL      1009.5691    1251.5862    7305293.0   18006621.0
MOLE FRACTION WATER (ENTRAINER FREE BASIS)                                   .049112    .107264

KTRAY=17    PRESSURE=   47.620   TEMP= 162.133    M= 3   N= 5    KNTRL(10)= 0
  COMP      VAPOR M/HR     LIQ M/HR    LIQ BTU/M    VAP BTU/M    VP/THETA     X (18)        Y       ALPHA       GAMMA       THETA
  PNTAN2      750.2905     750.2900    6503.4753   16765.3520      43.8322    .818033    .783370   2.471473    1.322906    .994187
  ETHANOL     160.0411     160.0374    4540.4524   21982.2030      12.2352    .174487    .167097   1.000000    1.917584    .941578
  WATER        47.4410       6.8606    2313.3971   20382.2610       5.2050    .007480    .049533   5.739363   25.870892    .958204
  TOTAL       957.7726     917.1880    5622309.8   17063895.0
MOLE FRACTION WATER (ENTRAINER FREE BASIS)                                   .041106    .228651

KTRAY=18    PRESSURE=   47.480   TEMP= 160.367    M= 1   N= 5    KNTRL(10)= 0
  COMP      VAPOR M/HR     LIQ M/HR    LIQ BTU/M    VAP BTU/M    VP/THETA     X (19)        Y       ALPHA       GAMMA       THETA
  PNTAN2      777.9226     777.9222    6244.8645   16719.4820      42.8265    .847792    .811883   1.269234    1.100325    .991243
  ETHANOL     130.7335     130.7299    4328.2252   21953.7990      11.7269    .142472    .136441   1.000000    3.165983    .943219
  WATER        49.5142       8.9337    2207.3051   20369.4990       4.9839    .009736    .051676   8.834945   65.815821    .959426
  TOTAL       958.1704     917.5858    5443553.7   16885141.0
MOLE FRACTION WATER (ENTRAINER FREE BASIS)                                   .063966    .274701

FINAL RESULTS FOLLOW


PROGRAM HAS CALCULATED THE FOLLOWING VARIABLES

FEED        COMP(1)     MOLES/HR                              V( 1) =   .00000000
FEED        COMP(2)     MOLES/HR                              V( 2) =   .24202000+03
FEED        COMP(3)     MOLES/HR                              V( 3) =   .40581588+02
FEED        TOTAL       MOLES/HR                              V( 4) =   .28260159+03
BOTTOMS     COMP(1)     MOLES/HR                              V( 5) =   .15005057-03
BOTTOMS     COMP(2)     MOLES/HR                              V( 6) =   .24201635+03
BOTTOMS     COMP(3)     MOLES/HR                              V( 7) =   .56181042-03
BOTTOMS     TOTAL       MOLES/HR                              V( 8) =   .24201705+03
DISTILLATE  COMP(1)     MOLES/HR                              V( 9) =   .40584534-03
DISTILLATE  COMP(2)     MOLES/HR                              V(10) =   .36526080-02
DISTILLATE  COMP(3)     MOLES/HR                              V(11) =   .40580475+02
DISTILLATE  TOTAL       MOLES/HR                              V(12) =   .40584534+02
COMP(1) VAPOR-LIQUID FLOW STRIPPING SECTION     MOLES/HR V(13) =  -.15005057-03
COMP(2) VAPOR-LIQUID FLOW STRIPPING SECTION     MOLES/HR V(14) =  -.24201635+03
COMP(3) VAPOR-LIQUID FLOW STRIPPING SECTION     MOLES/HR V(15) =  -.56181042-03
```

```
                    HEAT FLOW STRIPPING SECTION      BTU/HR  V(16) =  .10701400+08
COMP(1) VAPOR-LIQUID FLOW RECTIFYING SECTION   MOLES/HR V(17) =  .40584534-03
COMP(2) VAPOR-LIQUID FLOW RECTIFYING SECTION   MOLES/HR V(18) =  .36526080-02
COMP(3) VAPOR-LIQUID FLOW RECTIFYING SECTION   MOLES/HR V(19) =  .40580475+02
                    HEAT FLOW RECTIFYING SECTION     BTU/HR  V(20) =  .11441642+08
```

```
        VAPOR MOLES AND ENTHALPIES ARE FLOWS FROM THE TRAY
        LIQUID MOLES AND ENTHALPIES ARE FLOWS  TO   THE TRAY
```

Computer Output Page 12

```
                    LIQUID AND VAPOR COMPOSITIONS ARE FOR THE FLOWS FROM THE TRAY
```

```
REBOILER   PRESSURE= 50.000   TEMP= 234.910
COMP       VAPOR M/HR    LIQ M/HR    LIQ BTU/M    VAP BTU/M    VP/THETA      X          Y         ALPHA       GAMMA       THETA
PNTAN2        .0059        .0061     9961.3993   18655.6430   .983158+02   .000001    .000007   .119476+02  .607608+01  .114654+01
ETHNOL     799.9920     1042.0083    7455.5545   23087.8140   .499997+02   .999997    .999990   .100000+01  .100000+01  .999999-00
WATER         .0021        .0026     3653.9526   20883.2230   .231712+02   .000002    .000003   .111692+01  .241012+01  .983621-00
TOTAL      800.0000     1042.0170    7768820.1   18470220.0
MOLE FRACTION WATER (ENTRAINER FREE BASIS)                                 .000002    .000003

KTRAY=  1  PRESSURE= 49.860   TEMP= 234.748   M= 2   N= 5
COMP       VAPOR M/HR    LIQ M/HR    LIQ BTU/M    VAP BTU/M    VP/THETA      X          Y         ALPHA       GAMMA       THETA
PNTAN2        .0558        .0559     9944.2387   18651.4540   .981421+02   .000006    .000070   .119698+02  .608071+01  .114642+01
ETHNOL     799.1022     1041.1186    7440.7544   23085.5050   .498567+02   .999992    .999927   .100000+01  .100000+01  .999994-00
WATER         .0023        .0028     3647.6417   20882.1670   .251020+02   .000003    .000003   .111699+01  .241059+01  .983646-00
TOTAL      799.1602     1041.1773    7747273.7   18448765.0
MOLE FRACTION WATER (ENTRAINER FREE BASIS)                                 .000003    .000003

KTRAY=  2  PRESSURE= 49.720   TEMP= 234.558   M= 2   N= 6
COMP       VAPOR M/HR    LIQ M/HR    LIQ BTU/M    VAP BTU/M    VP/THETA      X          Y         ALPHA       GAMMA       THETA
PNTAN2        .5139        .5141     9921.9861   18646.5080   .979429+02   .000054    .000644   .119933+02  .608470+01  .114621+01
ETHNOL     797.7091     1039.7254    7421.5674   23082.7760   .496905+02   .999944    .999353   .100000+01  .100000+01  .999943-00
WATER         .0024        .0030     3639.4535   20880.9200   .230212+02   .000003    .000003   .111717+01  .241138+01  .983646-00
TOTAL      798.2254     1040.2425    7721503.4   18422972.0
MOLE FRACTION WATER (ENTRAINER FREE BASIS)                                 .000003    .000003

KTRAY=  3  PRESSURE= 49.580   TEMP= 234.102   M= 2   N= 8
COMP       VAPOR M/HR    LIQ M/HR    LIQ BTU/M    VAP BTU/M    VP/THETA      X          Y         ALPHA       GAMMA       THETA
PNTAN2       4.6852       4.6854     9783.6962   18634.6550   .975110+02   .000494    .005912   .120282+02  .608261+01  .114519+01
ETHNOL     787.8411     1029.8574    7302.4418   23076.2360   .493110+02   .999503    .994085   .100000+01  .100000+01  .999483-00
WATER         .0025        .0031     3588.4516   20877.9290   .228338+02   .000003    .000003   .111836+01  .241516+01  .983429-00
TOTAL      792.5288     1034.5459    7566325.0   18267766.0
MOLE FRACTION WATER (ENTRAINER FREE BASIS)                                 .000003    .000003

KTRAY=  4  PRESSURE= 49.440   TEMP= 231.260   M= 3   N= 5
COMP       VAPOR M/HR    LIQ M/HR    LIQ BTU/M    VAP BTU/M    VP/THETA      X          Y         ALPHA       GAMMA       THETA
PNTAN2      39.8050      39.8052     8858.5103   18560.8360   .950046+02   .004529    .052418   .121590+02  .602307+01  .113705+01
ETHNOL     719.5733     961.5896     6510.6443   23035.3850   .470586+02   .995468    .947579   .100000+01  .100006+01  .995459-00
WATER         .0024        .0030     3241.9305   20859.2590   .217125+02   .000003    .000003   .112886+01  .244678+01  .981333-00
TOTAL      759.3808     1001.3978    6613192.3   17314512.0
MOLE FRACTION WATER (ENTRAINER FREE BASIS)                                 .000003    .000003

KTRAY=  5  PRESSURE= 49.300   TEMP= 211.961   M= 3   N= 5
COMP       VAPOR M/HR    LIQ M/HR    LIQ BTU/M    VAP BTU/M    VP/THETA      X          Y         ALPHA       GAMMA       THETA
PNTAN2     268.0904     268.0906     7318.0396   18059.5690   .787405+02   .039750    .341087   .125051+02  .537254+01  .108614+01
```

```
ETHNOL       517.8967       759.9131      523.8250   22752.8710   .336685+02      .960247    .658911 .100000+01 .100477+01 .971859-00
WATER           .0020          .0026     2642.8492   20730.5130   .151609+02      .000003    .000003 .123329+01 .275187+01 .969674-00
TOTAL        785.9892      1028.0062     5923958.0   16625276.4
MOLE FRACTION WATER (ENTRAINER FREE BASIS)                                        .000003    .000004

KTRAY=  6   PRESSURE=   49.160   TEMP= 178.640    M= 3    N= 5
COMP         VAPOR M/HR     LIQ M/HR      LIQ BTU/M    VAP BTU/M    VP/THETA        X          Y        ALPHA      GAMMA      THETA
PNTAN2       656.3955       656.3956      6894.4591   17194.0960   .541901+02      .260787    .690351 .631956+01 .240146+01 .101820+01
ETHNOL       294.4158       536.4321      4862.3906   22244.0940   .175479+02      .739211    .309646 .100000+01 .117350+01 .947050-00
WATER           .0022          .0028     2472.8385   20500.1590   .759450+01      .000002    .000002 .222579+01 .603523+01 .959809-00

TOTAL        950.8135      1192.8395     7133842.3   17835185.0
MOLE FRACTION WATER (ENTRAINER FREE BASIS)                                        .000003    .000007

KTRAY=  7   PRESSURE=   49.020   TEMP= 169.194    M= 3    N= 3
COMP         VAPOR M/HR     LIQ M/HR      LIQ BTU/M    VAP BTU/M    VP/THETA        X          Y        ALPHA      GAMMA      THETA
PNTAN2       792.9419       792.9420      6817.9567   16948.7490   .482035+02      .550284    .781714 .292673+01 .144463+01 .100173+01
ETHNOL       221.4156       463.4319      4799.1707   22095.0280   .143011+02      .449714    .218281 .100000+01 .166373+01 .944806-00
WATER           .0050          .0056     2442.8741   20432.9990   .612900+01      .000002    .000005 .441599+01 .171431+02 .959835-00
TOTAL       1014.3625      1256.3795     7630346.8   18331659.0
MOLE FRACTION WATER (ENTRAINER FREE BASIS)                                        .000005    .000023

KTRAY=  8   PRESSURE=   48.880   TEMP= 167.474    M= 2    N= 7
COMP         VAPOR M/HR     LIQ M/HR      LIQ BTU/M    VAP BTU/M    VP/THETA        X          Y        ALPHA      GAMMA      THETA
PNTAN2       824.6641       824.6642      6797.2936   16904.0770   .471540+02      .631133    .801782 .236421+01 .131689+01 .998997-00
ETHNOL       203.8620       445.8783      4782.1087   22067.6550   .137553+02      .368863    .198205 .100000+01 .190947+01 .945259-00
WATER           .0131          .0137     2433.4969   20420.6820   .588661+01      .000004    .000013 .532861+01 .237755+02 .960357-00
TOTAL       1028.5392      1270.5562     7737756.5   18439207.0
MOLE FRACTION WATER (ENTRAINER FREE BASIS)                                        .000012    .000064

KTRAY=  9   PRESSURE=   48.740   TEMP= 167.009    M= 2    N= 6
COMP         VAPOR M/HR     LIQ M/HR      LIQ BTU/M    VAP BTU/M    VP/THETA        X          Y        ALPHA      GAMMA      THETA
PNTAN2       831.2025       831.2026      6786.5001   16891.9910   .468633+02      .649058    .806073 .224776+01 .129165+01 .998512-00
ETHNOL       199.9386       441.9550      4773.1986   22060.2390   .136104+02      .350932    .193894 .100000+01 .197858+01 .945469-00
WATER           .0341          .0347     2429.1187   20417.3450   .582269+01      .000011    .000033 .556344+01 .257304+02 .960537-00
TOTAL       1031.1753      1273.1922     7750579.6   18452055.0
MOLE FRACTION WATER (ENTRAINER FREE BASIS)                                        .000031    .000171

KTRAY= 10   PRESSURE=   48.600   TEMP= 166.766    M= 2    N= 6
COMP         VAPOR M/HR     LIQ M/HR      LIQ BTU/M    VAP BTU/M    VP/THETA        X          Y        ALPHA      GAMMA      THETA
PNTAN2       832.4716       832.4717      6777.2436   16885.6750   .467014+02      .652849    .807122 .222596+01 .128657+01 .998423-00
ETHNOL       198.8485       440.8649      4765.5584   22056.3600   .135342+02      .347124    .192793 .100000+01 .199440+01 .945570-00
WATER           .0877          .0883     2425.3626   20415.6010   .578907+01      .000027    .000085 .562155+01 .262115+02 .960616-00
TOTAL       1031.4078      1273.4248     7743044.8   18444509.0
MOLE FRACTION WATER (ENTRAINER FREE BASIS)                                        .000078    .000441

KTRAY= 11   PRESSURE=   48.460   TEMP= 164.557    M= 2    N= 6
COMP         VAPOR M/HR     LIQ M/HR      LIQ BTU/M    VAP BTU/M    VP/THETA        X          Y        ALPHA      GAMMA      THETA
PNTAN2       832.5859       832.5860      6767.7421   16880.2570   .465613+02      .653727    .807480 .222373+01 .128557+01 .998405-00
ETHNOL       198.2818       440.2982      4757.7173   22053.0310   .134698+02      .346204    .192303 .100000+01 .199838+01 .945640-00
WATER           .2240          .2246     2421.5060   20414.1040   .576065+01      .000069    .000217 .564222+01 .263643+02 .960670-00
TOTAL       1031.0917      1273.1087     7730085.3   18431551.0
MOLE FRACTION WATER (ENTRAINER FREE BASIS)                                        .000200    .001128
```

Computer Output Page 13

```
KTRAY= 12   PRESSURE=  48.320   TEMP= 166.343   M= 2   N= 6
 COMP      VAPOR M/HR    LIQ M/HR    LIQ BTU/M    VAP BTU/M    VP/THETA        X         Y       ALPHA       GAMMA        THETA
 PNTAN2     832.2150    832.2152    6756.8310    16874.6930   .464180+02    .653979    .807602  .222620+01  .128551+01  .998385-00
 ETHNOL     197.6918    439.7081    4748.7144    22049.6130   .134043+02    .345845    .191845  .100000+01  .199964+01  .945688-00
 WATER         .5703        .5708   2417.0756    20412.5660   .573175+01    .000176    .000553  .565548+01  .264472+02  .960708-00
 TOTAL     1030.4771   1272.4941   7712565.2    18414041.0
 MOLE FRACTION WATER (ENTRAINER FREE BASIS)                                  .000510    .002876

KTRAY= 13   PRESSURE=  48.180   TEMP= 166.097   M= 2   N= 6
 COMP      VAPOR M/HR    LIQ M/HR    LIQ BTU/M    VAP BTU/M    VP/THETA        X         Y       ALPHA       GAMMA        THETA
 PNTAN2     831.1006    831.1008    6742.1831    16868.3020   .462556+02    .654003    .807425  .223160+01  .128596+01  .998324-00
 ETHNOL     196.7734    438.7897    4736.6308    22045.6850   .133303+02    .345548    .191168  .100000+01  .199956+01  .945688-00
 WATER        1.4478       1.4483   2411.1252    20410.7990   .569890+01    .000449    .001407  .566762+01  .265084+02  .960717-00
 TOTAL     1029.3218   1271.3388   7685310.7    18386810.0
 MOLE FRACTION WATER (ENTRAINER FREE BASIS)                                  .001296    .007304

KTRAY= 14   PRESSURE=  48.040   TEMP= 165.766   M= 2   N= 7
```

Computer Output Page 14

```
 COMP      VAPOR M/HR    LIQ M/HR    LIQ BTU/M    VAP BTU/M    VP/THETA        X         Y       ALPHA       GAMMA        THETA
 PNTAN2     828.2288    828.2290    6718.2870    16859.7180   .460426+02    .653721    .806559  .224263+01  .128732+01  .998153-00
 ETHNOL     194.9825    436.9988    4716.9242    22040.4060   .132332+02    .345140    .189881  .100000+01  .199722+01  .945570-00
 WATER        3.6558       3.6564   2401.4117    20408.4250   .565557+01    .001139    .003560  .568041+01  .265457+02  .960652-00
 TOTAL     1026.8671   1268.8842   7634350.7    18335807.0
 MOLE FRACTION WATER (ENTRAINER FREE BASIS)                                  .003290    .018404

KTRAY= 15   PRESSURE=  47.900   TEMP= 165.227   M= 3   N= 3
 COMP      VAPOR M/HR    LIQ M/HR    LIQ BTU/M    VAP BTU/M    VP/THETA        X         Y       ALPHA       GAMMA        THETA
 PNTAN2     821.2204    821.2205    6672.9946    16845.7060   .457047+02    .652722    .804006  .226759+01  .129094+01  .997709-00
 ETHNOL     191.0846    433.1010    4679.5937    22031.7840   .130792+02    .344396    .187079  .100000+01  .198941+01  .945163-00
 WATER        9.1057       9.1062   2382.9789    20404.5470   .558635+01    .002882    .008915  .569528+01  .265271+02  .960408-00
 TOTAL     1021.4107   1263.4277   7528436.8    18229770.0
 MOLE FRACTION WATER (ENTRAINER FREE BASIS)                                  .008298    .045485

NEXT TRAY IS FEED TRAY


KTRAY= 16   PRESSURE=  47.760   TEMP= 164.203   M= 3   N= 4
 COMP      VAPOR M/HR    LIQ M/HR    LIQ BTU/M    VAP BTU/M    VP/THETA        X         Y       ALPHA       GAMMA        THETA
 PNTAN2     805.1856    805.1857    6581.6141    16819.1180   .450731+02    .649994    .797554  .232732+01  .130017+01  .996623-00
 ETHNOL     182.4605    424.4768    4604.3625    22015.4040   .127925+02    .342798    .180731  .100000+01  .196836+01  .944075-00
 WATER       21.9231      21.9236   2345.7019    20397.1830   .545688+01    .007208    .021715  .571457+01  .263694+02  .959741-00
 TOTAL     1009.5691   1251.5862   7305293.0    18006621.0
 MOLE FRACTION WATER (ENTRAINER FREE BASIS)                                  .020593    .107264

KTRAY= 17   PRESSURE=  47.620   TEMP= 162.133   M= 3   N= 5
 COMP      VAPOR M/HR    LIQ M/HR    LIQ BTU/M    VAP BTU/M    VP/THETA        X         Y       ALPHA       GAMMA        THETA
 PNTAN2     750.2905    750.2900    6503.8753    16765.3520   .438322+02    .643332    .783370  .247147+01  .132291+01  .994187-00
 ETHNOL     160.0411    160.0374    4540.4524    21982.2030   .122352+02    .339151    .167097  .100000+01  .191758+01  .941578-00
 WATER       47.4410       6.8606   2313.8971    20382.2610   .520498+01    .017517    .049533  .573936+01  .258709+02  .958204-00
 TOTAL      957.7726    917.1880   5622309.8    17063895.0
 MOLE FRACTION WATER (ENTRAINER FREE BASIS)                                  .049112    .228651
```

```
KTRA= 18   PRESSURE=  47.480   TEMP= 160.367    M= 1   N= 5
COMP       VAPOR M/HR    LIQ M/HR    LIQ BTU/M    VAP BTU/M    VP/THETA        X         Y        ALPHA        GAMMA       THETA
PNTAN2      777.9226     777.9222    6244.8645    16719.4820   .428265+02   .818033   .811883  .126923+01  .110033+01  .991243-00
ETHNOL      130.7335     130.7299    4328.1252    21953.7990   .117269+02   .174487   .136441  .100000+01  .316598+01  .943219-00
WATER        49.5142       8.9337    2207.3051    20369.4990   .498386+01   .007480   .051676  .883494+01  .658158+02  .959426-00
TOTAL       958.1704     917.5858    5443553.7    16885141.0
MOLE FRACTION WATER (ENTRAINER FREE BASIS)                                  .041106   .274701

          ACCUMULATOR AND HEATER OR SUBCOOLER CALCULATIONS          CYCLE NO 1                    Computer Output Page 15


ACCUMULATOR

    VAPOR-LIQUID EQUILIBRIA FOR ORGANIC PHASE        PRESSURE=  44.815     TEMP= 154.450
    COMP       X         Y          K          ALPHA        GAMMA       THETA     VP/THETA
    PNTAN2   .876890   .808694   .922230-00   .975464-00  .105166+01  .98874-00  .39300+02
    ETHNOL   .115232   .108944   .945427-00   .100000+01  .414479+01  .94295-00  .10222+02
    WATER    .007878   .082362   .10455C+02   .110584+02  .108402+03  .95940-00  .43223+01

    VAPOR-LIQUID EQUILIBRIA FOR AQUEOUS PHASE        PRESSURE=  44.814     TEMP= 154.450
    COMP       X         Y          K          ALPHA        GAMMA       THETA     VP/THETA
    PNTAN2   .001251   .808692   .646451+03   .148266+04  .737158+03  .98874-00  .39300+02
    ETHNOL   .249871   .108946   .436007-00   .100000+01  .191141+01  .94295-00  .10222+02
    WATER    .748878   .082363   .109981+00   .252247-00  .114030+01  .95940-00  .43223+01

    FRACTION OF AQUEOUS PHASE = .059107

                                          TOTAL HEAT =  .55574808+07 BTU/HR
                              CONDENSER   HEAT LOAD = -.11327660+08 BTU/HR


NO HEATER OR SUBCOOLER

FRACTION OF AQUEOUS PHASE TO SATISFY WATER BALANCE = .95661-22-00                                 Computer Output Page 16


ENTRAINER MAKE-UP = .40584534-03 M/HR


PRODUCT OUT ---

    COMP      PRODUCT M/HR
    PNTAN2        .0004
    ETHNOL        .0037
    WATER       40.5805
    TOTAL       40.5845
```

Table II. Column Profiles in Azeotropic Distillation

Dehydration of Aqueous Ethanol
Using n-Pentane as Entrainer

Tray No. (Equil.)	t, °F	Pressure, psia	Fraction Pentane in Liquid	Fraction Water in Vapor (Pentane-Free)	Fraction Ethanol in Liquid
18	160.37	47.48	0.818	0.275	0.175
17	162.13	47.62	0.643	0.229	0.339
16[a]	164.20	47.76	0.650	0.107	0.343
15	165.23	47.90	0.653	0.045	0.344
14	165.77	48.04	0.654	0.018	0.345
13	166.10	48.18	0.654	0.0073	0.346
12	166.34	48.32	0.654	0.0029	0.346
11	166.56	48.46	0.654	0.0011	0.346
10	166.77	48.60	0.653	0.00044	0.347
9	167.01	48.74	0.649	0.00017	0.351
8	167.47	48.88	0.631	0.000064	0.369
7	169.19	49.02	0.550	0.000023	0.450
6	178.64	49.16	0.261	0.000007	0.739
5	211.96	49.30	0.040	0.000004	0.960
4	231.26	49.44	0.0045	0.000003	0.996
3	234.10	49.58	0.00049	0.000003	0.9995
2	234.56	49.72	0.00005	0.000003	0.99994
1	234.75	49.86	0.000006	0.000003	0.999992
Reboiler	234.91	50.00	0.000001	0.000003	0.999997

Bottom Product, Mole fraction ethanol = 0.99999706
Mole fraction water = 0.00000232
Mole fraction pentane = 0.00000062

Stripped Water Product, Mole fraction water = 0.99999
Mole fraction ethanol = 0.000009
Mole fraction pentane = 0.000001

Feed, 85.64%m ethanol, 14.36%m water

[a] Tray No. 16 is the feed tray.

The temperature profile is most clearly seen in Figure 1. The temperature changes slightly from the reboiler up a few trays; then it drops rapidly for about three trays. After this it drops only five degrees in the next nine trays and slowly drops another four degrees from the feed to the top tray.

The behavior of the temperature profile is explained when the composition profiles of Figure 2 are examined. In the first few trays near the reboiler, the concentration of ethanol in the liquid is high, above 99 mole %. From tray 4 to tray 7 the ethanol concentration drops from 99.6–45.0 mole %. In this same region the pentane concentration increases from approximately 0.5–55.0 mole %. The water concentration,

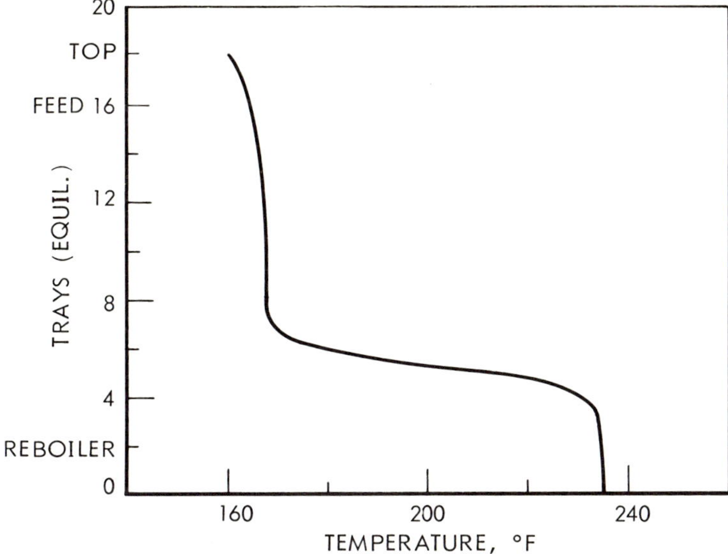

Figure 1.   Temperature profile for 50 psia column dehydration of aqueous ethanol using n-pentane

n-pentane-to-ethanol ratio 3.22 (mole basis)

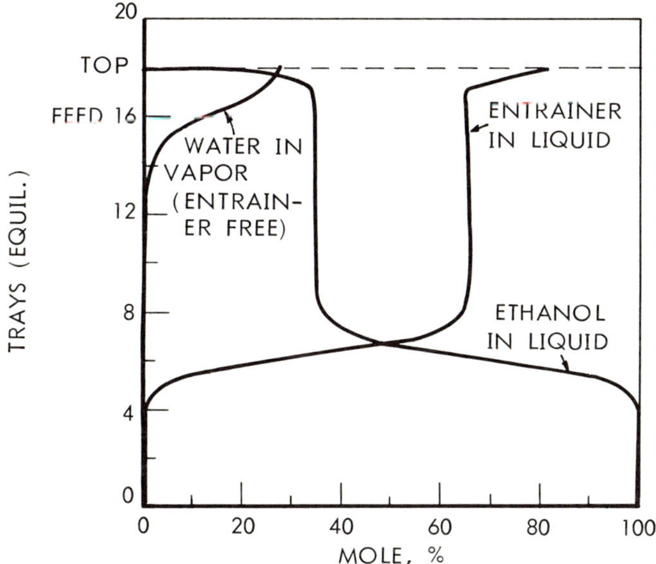

Figure 2.   Composition profiles in 50 psia column dehydration of aqueous ethanol using n-pentane

n-pentane-to-ethanol ratio 3.22 (mole basis)

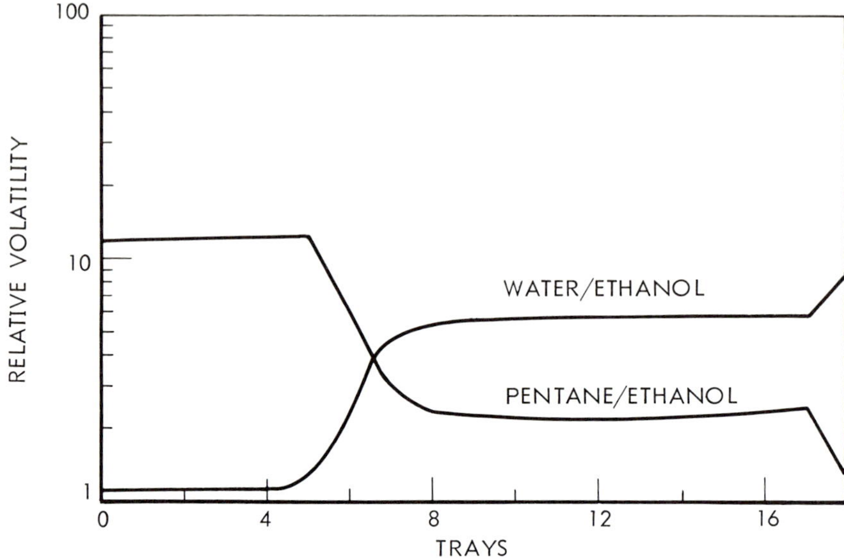

Figure 3.   Relative volatility profiles in 50 psia column dehydration of aqueous ethanol using n-pentane
n-pentane-to-ethanol ratio 3.22 (mole basis)

which is low, begins to increase. From tray 8 to tray 17 water continues to build up in the vapor on a pentane-free basis. Over this region the concentration of pentane in the liquid is nearly constant while the ethanol concentration decreases slowly. On the top two trays pentane increases and ethanol decreases in the liquid while water continues to build up in the vapor.

Figure 3 gives the relative volatility profiles also for the sample column calculation; these correspond to the temperature and composition profiles of Figures 1 and 2. Pentane is easily separated from ethanol while water is not as readily separated in the bottom of the column, reboiler to tray 5. The pentane volatility decreases and that of water increases rapidly, relative to ethanol, on proceeding from tray 5 to 8. They remain nearly constant for the next nine trays where the separation of water relative to ethanol is favorable; the separation of pentane relative to ethanol is still favorable in this region. On the top tray conditions are favorable for separating water, but for separating pentane they are less favorable.

It becomes difficult to remove ethanol from the top product. For the conditions of this sample calculation, the reduction of ethanol in the overhead vapors below about 13.5 mole % is accompanied by a building up of water in the overhead vapors and a tendency to form a second liquid phase in the top of the column.

The effect on tray requirements of changing the *n*-pentane-to-ethanol ratio is shown in Figure 4. The water content of the bottom product, ethanol, is shown *vs.* this ratio in Figure 5. With *n*-pentane as entrainer the water content of the ethanol product is reduced below ten ppm, on a mole basis.

Comparison of Entrainers

The choice of an entrainer used to make a desired separation in an azeotropic distillation depends on the binary mixture being separated and the nonidealities of these components with the added entrainer. While several different entrainers might be used to provide a separation, the final selection may depend on the required purity of the product. If several entrainers can produce a product of desired purity, the final choice may depend on an economic evaluation of the several schemes.

For the azeotropic dehydration of aqueous ethanol mixtures approaching the constant boiling mixture, a brief comparison is shown for the entrainers, *n*-pentane, benzene, and diethyl ether. Since water is most non-ideal in *n*-pentane, the driest ethanol is expected to be produced if *n*-pentane is used.

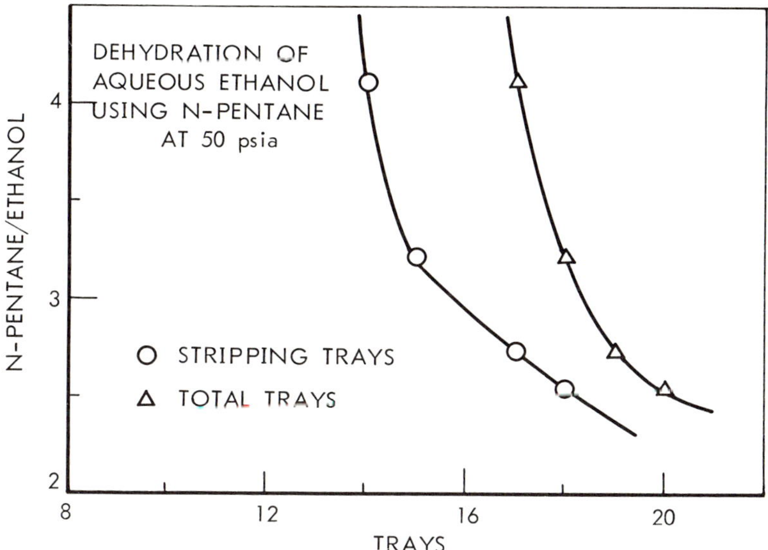

Figure 4.   Effect of changing the n-pentane-to-ethanol *ratio (mole basis) on trays required*

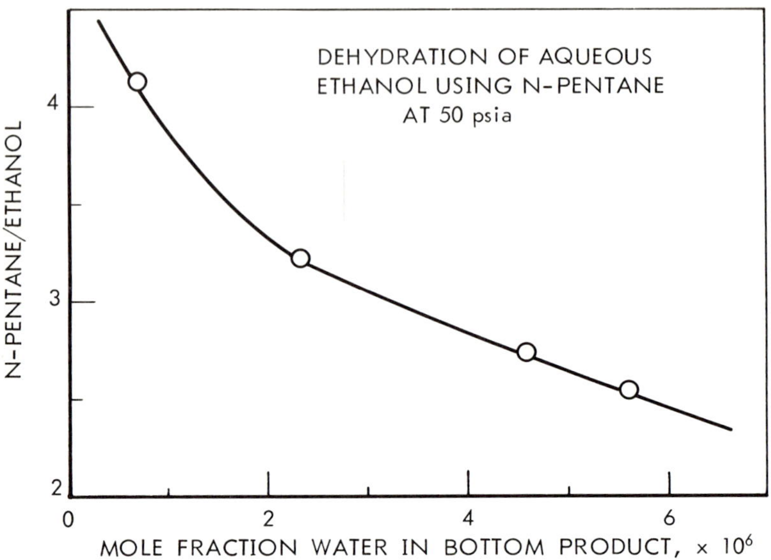

Figure 5.   Fraction water in bottom product ethanol vs. n-*pentane-to-ethanol ratio (mole basis)*

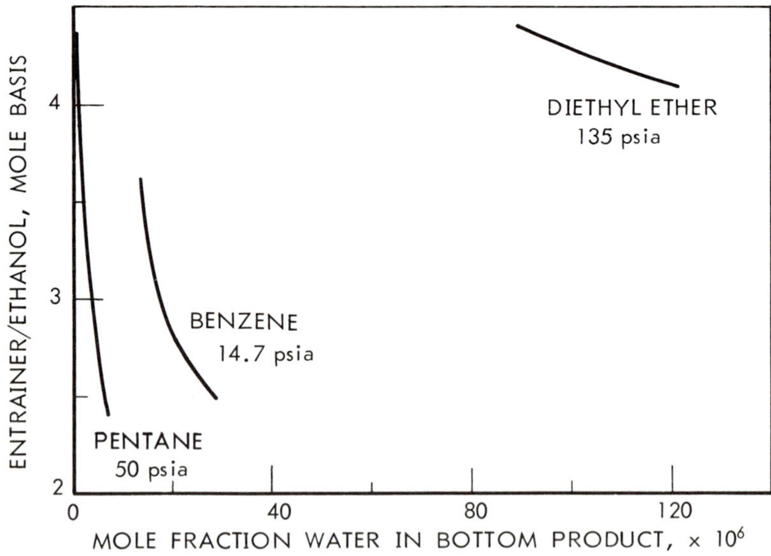

Figure 6.   Comparing entrainers, n-pentane, benzene, and diethyl ether, for water content of ethanol product

Calculations have been made using the automated feature of the Azeotropic Distillation Program ADP/ADPLLE. The same mole fraction of entrainer in the ethanol product, 0.62×10^{-6} has been used in calculations involving each entrainer. Using *n*-pentane, the azeotropic distillation was calculated for a column with a reboiler at 50 psia. The corresponding pressures were 14.7 psia and 135 psia for cases involving benzene and diethyl ether, respectively. Calculations were made also at higher pressures for cases using *n*-pentane and benzene. Although the above pressures are not necessarily the optimum for each solvent, comparisons have been made for the three cases as indicated.

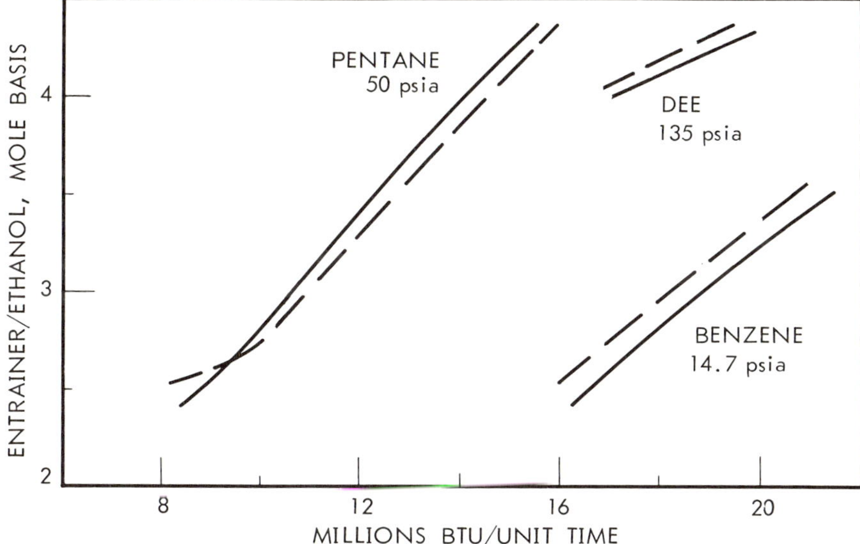

Figure 7.   Comparing the entrainers, n-*pentane, benzene, and diethyl ether, for reboiler and condenser loads in dehydrating aqueous ethanol*

——— Condenser loads, heat removed, btu/unit time
– – – Reboiler loads, heat added, btu/unit time

The calculated results, comparing the water content of the ethanol product for the entrainers, *n*-pentane, benzene, and diethyl ether, are shown in Figure 6. The mole fraction water in the ethanol product is plotted *vs.* the entrainer-to-ethanol ratio, on a mole basis. *n*-Pentane produces ethanol of lowest water content; benzene comes next, and diethyl ether comes last. Entrainer-to-ethanol ratios of 2.5–3.5, mole basis, are adequate when *n*-pentane or benzene is used; for diethyl ether, the ratio must be above four.

Condenser and reboiler loads are compared for the same three entrainers in Figure 7. For diethyl ether-to-ethanol ratios of about 4.2, the

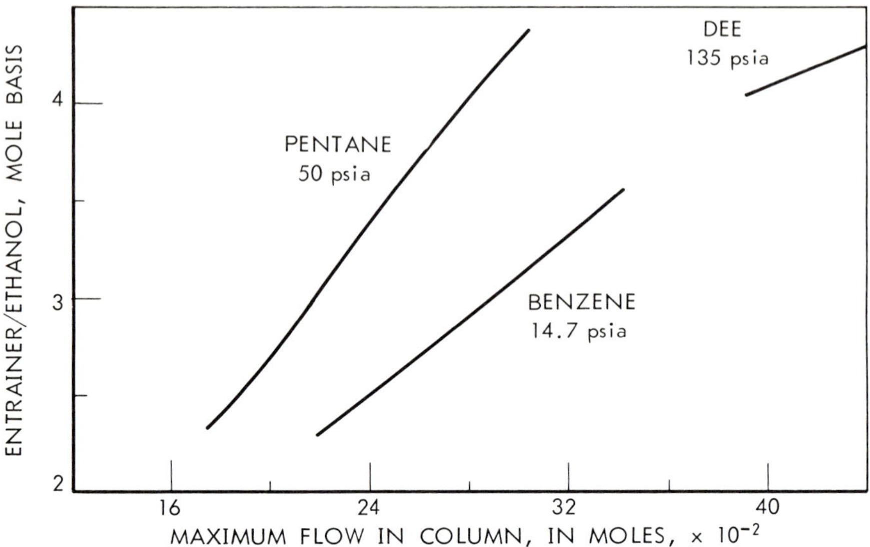

Figure 8. Comparison of maximum flows on any tray for entrainers, n-pentane, benzene, and diethyl ether, in dehydrating aqueous ethanol by azeotropic distillation

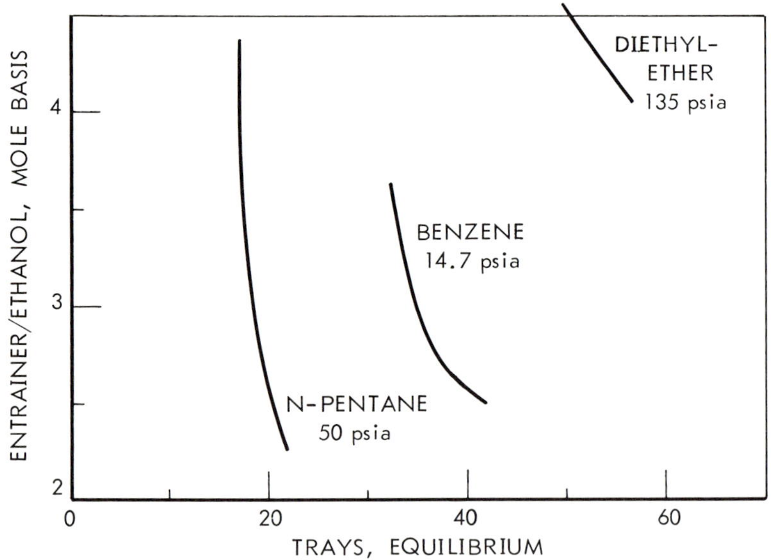

Figure 9. Comparing tray requirements for the entrainers, n-pentane, benzene, and diethyl ether, in dehydrating aqueous ethanol by azeotropic distillation

condenser and reboiler loads compare favorably with those for benzene-to-ethanol ratios of about 3, mole basis. At the higher ratio, heat loads with n-pentane are about 80% of those for diethyl ether. At the low ratio of about 3, the heat loads with n-pentane are only 60% of those for benzene.

The maximum flow on any tray in the column is compared for the three entrainers, n-pentane, benzene, and diethyl ether, in Figure 8. At the high entrainer-to-ethanol ratio of 4.2, the maximum flow when n-pentane is used is about 70% of that for the case using diethyl ether. For the low ratio of about 3, the flows with n-pentane are about 75% of those using benzene. A smaller diameter column is required with n-pentane than with either of the other entrainers.

Total tray requirements for the three entrainers are compared in Figure 9. The least number of trays is required when n-pentane is used; the most are required when diethyl ether is the entrainer. If benzene is used as entrainer at higher pressure than 14.7 psia, the corresponding curve in Figure 9 is shifted to the right, more trays being required.

The computer program for azeotropic distillation ADP/ADPLLE makes possible not only a comparison of entrainers for a separation but also gives results of a quality required for actual design calculations.

Acknowledgment

Some of the utility subroutines described here were designed after a general system of utility-subroutine programming developed by H. W. Brough of Shell Chemical Company. We also wish to acknowledge the support of E. G. Foster and L. J. Tichacek in facilitating this work.

List of Symbols

a_i	van der Waals attraction constant for component i
b_i	van der Waals covolume for component i
f_i^v	fugacity of component i in vapor-phase mixture
G_{ij}	$(a_i\xi_{io}{}^\circ)^{0.5} - (a_j\xi_j{}^\circ)^{0.5}$ $\overline{G}_{ij} = (a_i\overline{\xi}_i{}^\circ)^{0.5} - (a_j\overline{\xi}_j{}^\circ)^{0.5}$
K_i	Y_i/x_i ratio of vapor and liquid composition
P^*	a reference pressure
P	total pressure
$P_i{}^\circ$	vapor pressure for component i
V_i^l	liquid molar volume of component i
$\overline{V}_i^l$	partial molar volume of component i in liquid solution

X_i total liquid composition in region of two liquid phases

x_i liquid composition, mole fraction, polar phase

y_i liquid composition, mole fraction, nonpolar phase

Y_i vapor composition, mole fraction component i

α_{ij} volatility of component i relative to component j

γ_i liquid-phase activity coefficient, polar phase

Γ_i liquid-phase activity coefficient, nonpolar phase

δ_{ij} binary vapor interaction coefficient

θ_i imperfection-pressure coefficient

$\overset{*}{\xi}{}^{\circ}$ nonpolar part of the molecular attractive coefficient at zero pressure

$\bar{\xi}^{\circ}$ polar part of the molecular attraction coefficient at zero pressure

ξ° $\bar{\xi}^{\circ} + \overset{*}{\xi}{}^{\circ}$, the limiting value of the molecular attraction coefficient at zero pressure

$\phi_i{}^{\circ}$ fugacity coefficient for component i at saturation pressure Pi°

ϕ_i fugacity coefficient for component i in a vapor pressure

Literature Cited

1. Gerster, J. A., *Chem. Eng. Progr.* (1969) **65** (9), 43.
2. Hoffman, E. S., "Azeotropic and Extractive Distillation," Wiley, New York, 1964.
3. Robinson, C. S., Gilliland, E. R., "Elements of Fractional Distillation," p. 312, McGraw-Hill, New York, 1950.
4. Black, C., *Ind. Eng. Chem.* (1958) **50**, 391.
5. Black, C., *Ind. Eng. Chem.* (1958) **50**, 403.
6. Black, C., *A.I.Ch.E. J.* (1959) **5** (2), 251.
7. Black, C., *Ind. Eng. Chem.* (1959) **51**, 211.
8. Black, C., Derr, E. L., Papadopoulos, M. N., *Ind. Eng. Chem.* (1963) **55** (9), 38.
9. Null, H. R., Palmer, D. A., *Chem. Eng. Progr.* (1969) **65** (9), 47.
10. Yamada, I., S. Hidezumi, A. Kanji *Kagaku Kogaku* (1967) **31**, 395–398.
11. Berg, L., *Chem. Eng. Progr.* (1969) **65**, (9), 53.

RECEIVED November 24, 1970.

6

Prediction of Isobaric Vapor-Liquid Equilibrium Data for Mixtures of Water and Simple Alcohols

A. ANDIAPPAN and A. Y. McLEAN

Annamalainagas University, Tamifnedu, India and Nova Scotia Technical College, Halifax, Nova Scotia

The Non-Random, Two Liquid Equation was used in an attempt to develop a method for predicting isobaric vapor–liquid equilibrium data for multicomponent systems of water and simple alcohols—i.e., ethanol, 1-propanol, 2-methyl-1-propanol (2-butanol), and 3-methyl-1-butanol (isoamyl alcohol). Methods were developed to obtain binary equilibrium data indirectly from boiling point measurements. The binary data were used in the Non-Random, Two Liquid Equation to predict vapor–liquid equilibrium data for the ternary mixtures, water–ethanol–1-propanol, water–ethanol–2-methyl-1-propanol, and water–ethanol–3-methyl-1-butanol. Equilibrium data for these systems are reported.

The design of azeotropic or extractive distillation columns, as with conventional columns, demands a knowledge of the vapor–liquid equilibrium properties of the system to be distilled. Such knowledge is obtained experimentally or calculated from other properties of the components of the system. Since the systems in azeotropic or extractive distillation processes have at least three components, direct measurement of the equilibrium properties is laborious and, therefore, expensive, so methods of calculation of these data are desirable.

For azeotropic distillation especially the systems are non-ideal which makes calculating vapor–liquid equilibrium properties more difficult than, for example, in distillation of mixtures of simple hydrocarbons. Work predicting the vapor–liquid equilibrium properties of ternary mixtures of

93

water, ethanol, and one of the simple alcohols—*i.e.*, 1-propanol, 2-methyl-1-propanol, 3-methyl-1-butanol, (all form binary azeotropes with water) —is presented here.

Aqueous solutions of these alcohols occur when sugar solutions are fermented and may be separated by distilling the mixtures. It is a common, economically valuable process for manufacturing potable liquors and for producing industrial alcohol from fermented molasses solutions or pulp mill wastes. One of the authors (A.Y.M.) reports that design and operation of these columns is hampered by lack of vapor–liquid equilibrium data, especially for making potable liquors, where small amounts of the alcohols other than ethanol greatly affect the flavor and, therefore, the product's marketability.

Prediction of Vapor–Liquid Equilibrium Data

A system consisting of a liquid mixture and vapor is in equilibrium if, for any component i, the fugacities in the vapor and liquid phases, f_i^V and f_i^L are equal.

$$f_i^V = f_i^L \tag{1}$$

As the fugacities are not in themselves quantities which are easily established experimentally, it is necessary to relate them to easily determinable quantities—*e.g.*, temperature, pressure, and composition. This is done by introducing the fugacity and activity coefficients Φ_i and γ_i which are defined as follows,

$$\Phi_i = \frac{f_i^V}{y_i P} \text{ and } \gamma_i = \frac{f_i^L}{x_i f_i^{OL}} \tag{2}$$

where y_i is the composition of component i in the vapor phase, P is the total pressure of the system, x_i is the composition of component i in the liquid phase, and f_i^{OL} is the fugacity of component i in the liquid at a reference state. This reference state is the fugacity of pure liquid i at the temperature and pressure of the system. Equation 1 then becomes

$$\Phi_i y_i P = \gamma_i x_i f_i^{OL} \tag{3}$$

At conditions when it is safe to assume that the gas phase will behave in an ideal manner—*i.e.*, at low pressure with all components condensable—

$$\Phi_i \rightarrow 1 \text{ and } f_i^{OL} \rightarrow P_i^S$$

P_i^S is the vapor pressure of pure liquid i at the temperature of the system, and equilibrium is described by the equation,

$$y_i P = \gamma_i x_i P_i^S \tag{4}$$

At conditions where it is incorrect to assume ideal behavior for the gas phase, Φ_i and f_i^{OL} are calculated by procedures described by Prausnitz *et al.* (*1*).

The calculation of γ_i, the activity coefficient, establishes γ_i as a function of composition, as well as temperature and pressure. This is done by relating γ_i to the excess Gibbs energy G^E,—*i.e.*, by the equation

$$ln\ \gamma_i = \frac{1}{RT}\left(\frac{\delta G^E}{\delta n_i}\right)_{T,P,n_j \neq i} \tag{4a}$$

and expressing G^E or g^E, the molar excess Gibbs energy, in terms of composition.

The problem of expressing the excess Gibbs energy as a function of composition has been researched extensively, and many methods of varying accuracy and usefulness have been proposed. An extensive discussion of these methods is given by Hala *et al.* (*2*), who show that many common expressions—*e.g.*, those of van Laar and Margules—are deduced from the general expression of Wohl (*3*).

Cukor and Prausnitz (*4*), however, point out that Wohl's general expression precludes other expressions for the composition dependence of the excess free energy, including that of Wilson (*5*), which has been used by several authors to predict and correlate vapor–liquid equilibrium (*1, 6, 7*). Wilson's equation and the modification proposed by Renon and Prausnitz (*8*) use the local mole fraction concept, produced because molecules in solution aggregate as a result of the variation in intermolecular forces. The local mole fraction concept results in a more useful description of the behavior of molecules in a non-ideal mixture.

The Wilson Equation and the Non-Random Two-Liquid (NRTL) Equation

The Wilson equation, used by Prausnitz *et al.* (*1*) and other workers (*6, 7*), equals or surpasses earlier two-parameter equations in correlating vapor–liquid equilibrium data for a large number of non-ideal systems. The equation which is sufficiently discussed elsewhere (*1*) contains two adjustable parameters per binary and predicts multicomponent equilibrium data using the binary parameters only. No multicomponent experimental data are necessary as for the van Laar type equations of third order and above.

One limitation of the Wilson equation has been that it cannot be applied to systems where the non-ideality is such that two liquid phases are formed—*e.g.*, water–2-methyl-1-propanol and water–3-methyl-1-butanol.

Renon and Prausnitz (8) proposed another equation, based also on the local mole fraction concept, which would avoid this limitation and could be applied to partially miscible mixtures. The relationship between activity coefficient and liquid phase composition is given by the equation

$$ln\, \gamma_i = \frac{\sum\limits_{j=1}^{N} \omega_{ji} G_{ji} x_j}{\sum\limits_{k=1}^{N} G_{ki} x_k} + \sum_{j=1}^{N} \frac{x_j G_{ij}}{\sum\limits_{k=1}^{N} G_{kj} x_k} \left\{ \omega_{ij} - \frac{\sum\limits_{l=1}^{N} x_l \omega_{lj} G_{lj}}{\sum\limits_{k=1}^{N} G_{kj} x_k} \right\} \tag{5}$$

where N = number of components

$$\omega_{ji} = \frac{g_{ji} - g_{ii}}{RT} \qquad G_{ji} = \exp\,(-\alpha_{ji} \omega_{ji})$$

$(g_{ji} - g_{ii})$ is the adjustable parameter (two per binary) similar to that contained in the Wilson equation. α_{ji} is an empirical non-randomness parameter.

Renon and Prausnitz (8) recommend values of α_{ji} for various classes of mixtures. If these values are valid then Equation 5 has only two adjustable parameters per binary. The NRTL equation was used in this work.

Experimental

To test the NRTL equation for predicting VLE data for ternary mixtures, experimental data for the ternary mixtures and for the binary components of the mixtures are necessary. A literature survey showed that data were not readily available for any of the ternaries or for the two binaries ethanol–3-methyl-1-propanol and 3-methyl-1-butanol–water, and it was therefore necessary to obtain these data experimentally.

The direct measurement of vapor–liquid equilibrium data for partially miscible mixtures such as 3-methyl-1-butanol–water is difficult, and although stills have been designed for this purpose (9, 10), the data was indirectly obtained from measurements of pressure, P, temperature, t, and liquid composition, x. It was also felt that a test of the validity of the NRTL equation in predicting the VLE data for the ternary mixtures would be the successful prediction of the boiling point. This eliminates the complicated analytical procedures necessary in the direct measurement of ternary VLE data.

A modified version of the *M*-100 boiling point apparatus, made by the James F. Scanlon Co., Whittier, Calif. was used; temperature was measured by a Hewlett-Packard model 2801A quartz thermometer. All measurements were made at atmospheric pressure with the temperature corrected then to 760 mm Hg.

Table I.   Fugacity Coefficients

Component	Temperature, °C	Φ_i
Water	80	0.9925
	90	0.9960
	130	1.0150
	100	1.0000
Ethanol	80	1.0015
	90	1.0119
	100	1.0240
1-Propanol	80	0.9898
	90	0.9954
	100	1.0018
2-Methyl-1-propanol	80	0.9726
	90	0.9809
	100	0.9904
3-Methyl-1-butanol	80	0.9535
	90	0.9608
	100	0.9686
	130	0.9991

To extract y from P, t, x, data obtained for the binary system, a computer program using the NRTL equation was prepared. Upon receiving the input data—*i.e.*, P, x, t and a value of α, usually around 0.475 —values of the adjustable parameters $(g_{12}-g_{22})$ and $(g_{21}-g_{11})$ were assumed. The activity coefficients were calculated using Equation 5 and values of y were calculated using Equation 4. To justify using Equation 4, values of the fugacity coefficients were calculated. These values (Table I) are believed sufficiently near unity to permit that the effects of gas phase nonideality can be ignored. The sum of y_1 and y_2 was compared with unity, and the procedure was repeated until sum y was within agreed limits of unity. This program also allowed the calculating of binary energy parameters used in predicting properties of the ternary systems.

An additional program took the energy parameters of the binary systems making up ternary mixtures and calculated the boiling point of the ternary and the equilibrium composition of the vapor phase. Comparison of the measured boiling point with the predicted boiling point for the same composition and pressure was used as a criterion of successful performance of the NRTL equation.

To illustrate the consistency between the two programs, data for the ethanol–water system reported by Rieder and Thompson (*11*) were used. The first program estimated the values of the energy parameters and calculated the vapor-phase composition, y, with a root mean square deviation (RMSD) of 0.00847. The mean arithmetic deviation between the sum y and unity was 0.0064. The estimated parameters were used in the second program which predicted the same values of y and also predicted the temperature of the boiling mixture. The predicted and experimental temperature agreed with a RMSD value of 0.22°C.

The procedure establishing the vapor–liquid equilibrium data for the binary system was tested using the homogeneous system, 1-propanol–water, and the heterogeneous system, 2-methyl-1-propanol–water, using the data of Murti and VanWinkle (*12*) and Ellis and Garbett (*9*). The RMSD value between the experimental and the calculated values of y were 0.011 and 0.0155, respectively, The comparison between experimental and calculated VLE data is shown in Figure 1 and Fig-

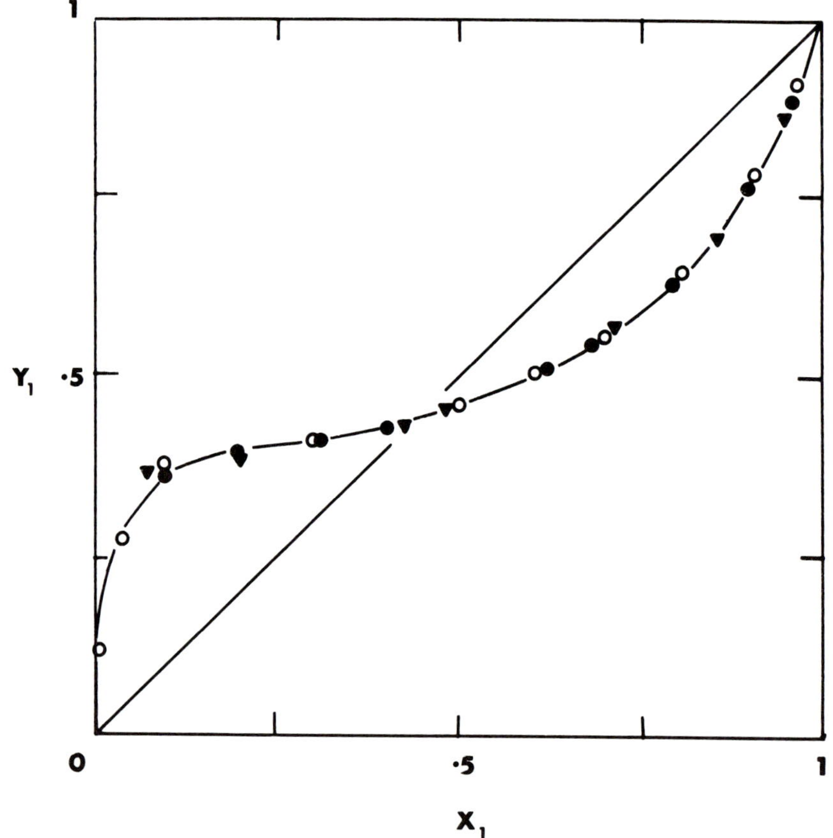

Figure 1. Comparison of calculated and experimental vapor–liquid equilibrium data at 760 mm Hg. 1-Propanol (1)–Water (2).

● *Indirectly measured, present work*
○ *Directly measured, Gadwa (15)*
▼ *Directly measured, Murti and Van Winkle (12)*

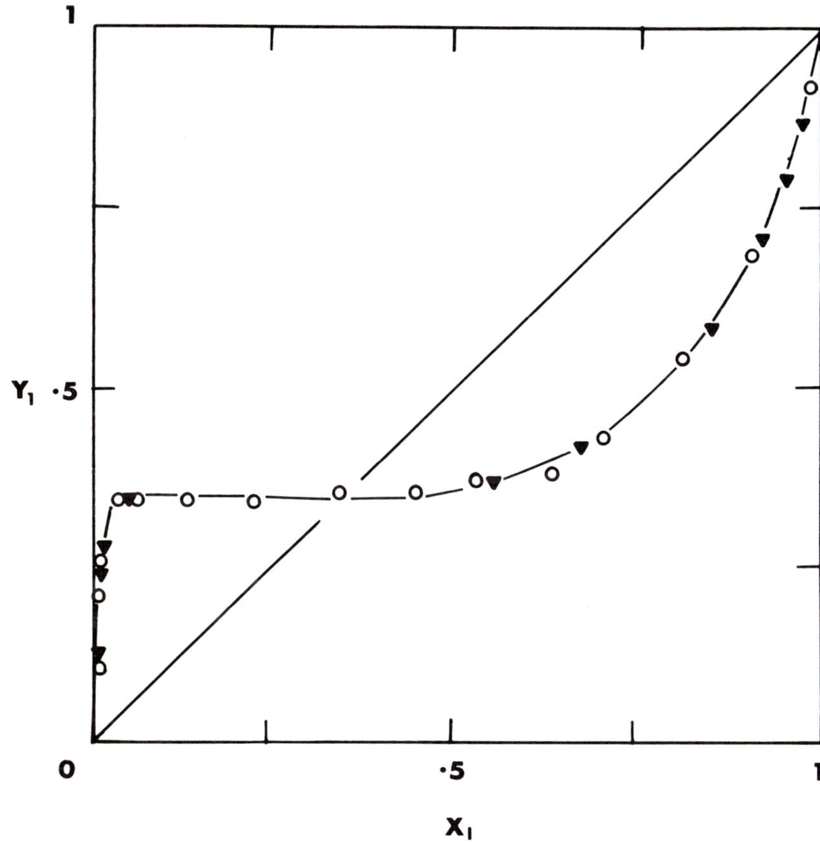

Figure 2.   Comparison of calculated and experimental vapor–liquid equilibrium data at 760 mm Hg. 2-Methyl-1-Propanol (1)–Water (2).

▼ *Indirectly measured, present work*
○ *Directly measured, Ellis and Garbett (9)*

ure 2, and they agree well enough to justify using the indirect method of establishing the VLE data on the system, ethanol–2-methyl-1-propanol and 3-methyl-1-butanol–water.

Direct measurement of the VLE data for the ethanol–2-methyl-1-propanol system were also made, using a MES100 model equilibrium supplied by the James F. Scanlon Co.

Results and Discussion

Binary System. The ethanol–2-methyl-propanol system was found to behave in an expected ideal way. The *x–y* data, that was directly

**Table II. Vapor–Liquid Equilibrium Data at 760 mm. Hg
Ethanol (1)–Methyl-1-Propanol (2)**

$t\,^{\circ}C$	x_1	y_1
104.15	0.050	0.126
101.88	0.080	0.200
101.55	0.085	0.215
101.03	0.090	0.235
98.07	0.155	0.332
94.67	0.220	0.460
94.08	0.243	0.479
90.96	0.330	0.595
89.34	0.382	0.658
87.56	0.465	0.712
86.75	0.490	0.742
86.11	0.510	0.770
85.24	0.560	0.790
84.18	0.610	0.817
83.67	0.635	0.845
82.54	0.705	0.875
81.45	0.770	0.915
81.11	0.800	0.920
80.06	0.870	0.950

**Table III. Vapor–Liquid Equilibrium Data at 760 mm. Hg
3-Methyl-1-Butanol (1)–Water (2)**

$t\,^{\circ}C$	x_1	y_1
99.17	0.0009	0.0155
97.99	0.0024	0.0386
97.82	0.0031	0.0482
96.60	0.0051	0.0725
96.27	0.0072	0.0932
96.14	0.0073	0.0942
95.90	0.0205	0.1603
95.26	0.0616	0.1694
97.32	0.5766	0.1810
104.03	0.6536	0.2323
109.86	0.7698	0.3495
119.65	0.8873	0.5710
125.76	0.9347	0.7158
126.96	0.9427	0.7449
128.54	0.9696	0.8512
129.84	0.9884	0.9394

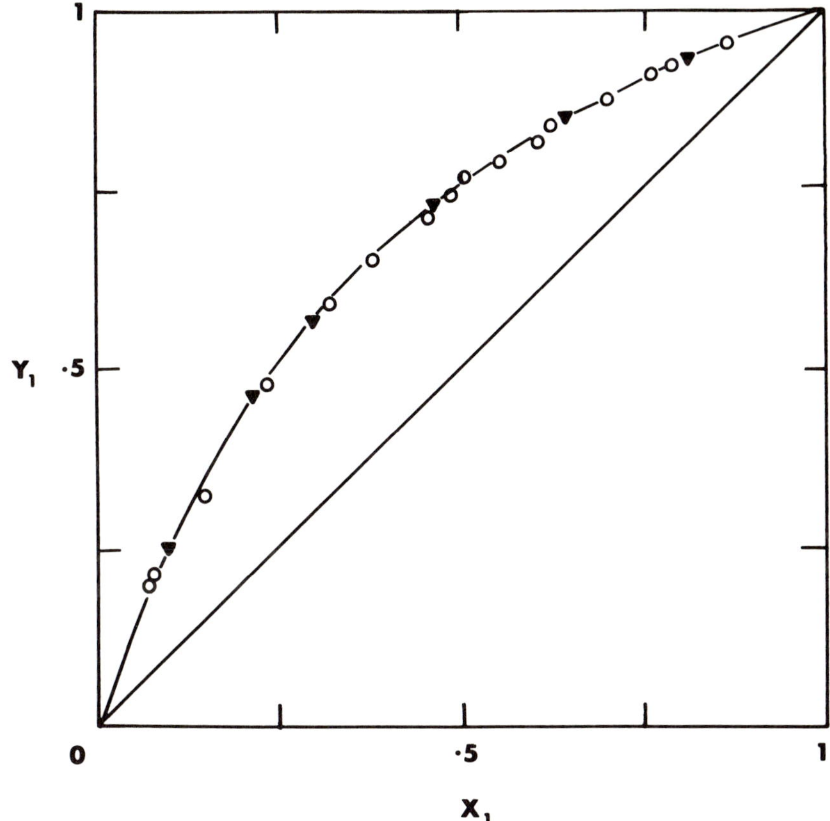

*Figure 3.   Vapor–liquid equilibrium data at 760 mm Hg. Ethanol (1)–
2-Methyl-1-Propanol (2).*

○ *Directly measured*
▼ *Indirectly measured*
— *Ideal behavior*

measured, are presented in Table II. Figure 3 shows the comparison
with the directly measured data, the indirectly measured data, and the
data calculated from Raoult's Law.

The vapor–liquid equilibrium data for the 3-methyl-1-butanol–water
system are shown in Table III and Figure 4. The boiling point measurements agreed with those reported in Timmermans (*13*). The value of
$\alpha = 0.45$ as suggested by Renon and Prausnitz (*8*) for alcohol–water
systems was not suitable. Various other values of α were tried, and a value
of $\alpha = 0.3$ was found to agree best. This fit can be established by using
the method described to test the consistency of the equations—*i.e.*, the

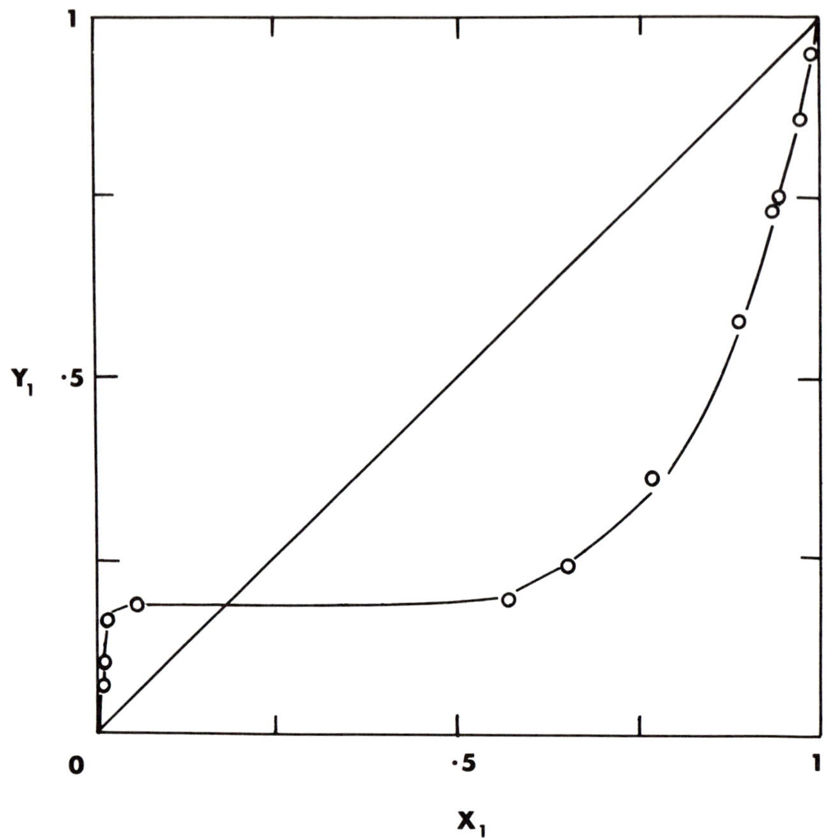

Figure 4. Vapor–liquid equilibrium data at 760 mm Hg. 3-Methyl-1-Butanol (1)–Water (2).

Table IV.   NRTL Parameters for the Binary Systems
Isobaric Systems at 1 Atm.

	Reference	α	$(g_{12}-g_{22})$ cal./gram mole	$(g_{21}-g_{11})$ cal./gram mole
Ethanol (1)–Water (2)	11	0.475	121.0	1161.5
1-Propanol (1)–Water (2)	15, 12	0.500	438.4	1762.9
2-Methyl-1-Propanol (1)–Water (2)	9	0.475	611.5	2475.7
3-Methyl-1-Butanol (1)–Water (2)	—	0.300	−386.9	3483.8
Ethanol (1)–1-Propanol (2)	16	0.500	465.5	−324.5
Ethanol (1)–3-Methyl-1-Butanol (2)	16	0.475	20.8	7.4
Ethanol (1)–2-Methyl-1-Propanol (2)	—	—	0	0

Table V.   Vapor–Liquid Equilibrium Data at 760 mm Hg
Water (1)–Ethanol (2)-1-Propanol (3)

x_1	x_2	$y_1{}^a$	$y_2{}^a$	$t\ °C^a$	$t\ °C^b$
0.1763	0.0905	0.3133	0.1353	89.13	89.07
0.3742	0.0992	0.4527	0.1426	86.70	86.40
0.5397	0.0944	0.5143	0.1503	86.14	85.60
0.7271	0.0987	0.5345	0.2100	85.75	85.46
0.1642	0.1920	0.2720	0.2730	87.57	87.65
0.3216	0.1949	0.3909	0.2649	85.55	85.47
0.4759	0.1966	0.4526	0.2828	84.63	84.57
0.6350	0.1984	0.4768	0.3395	84.04	83.94
0.1293	0.2698	0.2152	0.3752	86.89	87.19
0.2707	0.2956	0.3297	0.3822	84.47	84.59
0.4214	0.3123	0.3932	0.4123	83.12	83.12
0.5519	0.3076	0.4217	0.4510	82.54	82.51
0.1201	0.4024	0.1793	0.5203	84.85	85.12
0.2421	0.3935	0.2852	0.4857	83.30	83.45
0.3764	0.3777	0.3566	0.4750	82.43	82.47
0.4812	0.3934	0.3797	0.5214	81.60	81.52
0.1246	0.4861	0.1702	0.5966	83.47	83.79
0.2046	0.4837	0.2388	0.5744	82.42	82.65
0.3030	0.4944	0.2936	0.5797	81.35	81.47
0.4071	0.4939	0.3312	0.5994	80.63	80.67
0.0962	0.6059	0.1248	0.7064	82.14	82.39
0.1896	0.6054	0.2045	0.6785	80.92	81.03
0.3096	0.5907	0.2731	0.6652	80.03	80.01
0.0853	0.7030	0.1036	0.7814	80.94	81.11
0.1911	0.7026	0.1889	0.7518	79.65	79.68
0.1125	0.7007	0.1264	0.7691	80.59	80.01
0.1524	0.7319	0.1579	0.7792	79.69	79.30
0.0851	0.8319	0.0920	0.8648	79.24	79.07

[a] Predicted using NRTL equation.
[b] Measured.

calculation of the parameters with the first program and the use of the parameters to calculate the initial temperature.

Ternary System. The values of all binary parameters used in predicting the ternary data are shown in Table IV. The predicted values of the vapor–liquid equilibrium data—*i.e.*, the boiling point, and the composition of the vapor phase, y, for given values of the liquid composition, x, are presented in Tables V, VI, and VII. Also shown are the measured boiling points for the given values of the liquid composition. The RMSD value between the predicted and measured boiling points for the systems water–ethanol-1-propanol, water–ethanol–2-methyl-1-propanol, and water–ethanol–2-methyl-1-butanol are 0.23°C, 0.69°C, and 2.14°C. It seems therefore that since the NRTL equation successfully predicts temperature, the predicted values of y can be accepted confidently.

To test the method of predicting some directly measured ternary data, the predicted results for the system water–ethanol-1-propanol were used to calculate relative volatilities which were compared with the experimentally determined values of Carlson *et al.* (*14*). This comparison is shown on Figure 5. The comparison seems to indicate that the method of predicting is satisfactory and gives less scatter than the experimentally determined values of relative volatility.

Table VI.   Vapor–Liquid Equilibrium Data at 760 mm Hg
Water (*1*)–Ethanol (*2*)-2-Methyl-1-Propanol (*3*)

x_1	x_2	$y_1{}^a$	$y_2{}^a$	$t\,°C^b$	$t\,°C^b$
0.1937	0.0999	0.4203	0.1632	93.28	93.0
0.3582	0.1062	0.5294	0.1574	90.13	89.25
0.5377	0.1003	0.5945	0.1548	88.78	87.67
0.7115	0.1014	0.6098	0.1912	88.09	86.93
0.1589	0.2002	0.3300	0.3163	91.78	91.46
0.3156	0.1996	0.4521	0.2854	88.68	87.72
0.5570	0.1820	0.5377	0.2813	86.88	85.92
0.6352	0.2066	0.5208	0.3492	85.71	84.87
0.1264	0.3072	0.2468	0.4635	90.05	89.89
0.3006	0.2943	0.3947	0.4012	86.86	86.09
0.4103	0.3056	0.4323	0.4161	85.33	84.59
0.5562	0.2981	0.4572	0.4474	84.09	85.1
0.1255	0.3990	0.2158	0.5602	87.85	87.76
0.2611	0.3974	0.3274	0.5145	85.24	85.09
0.3722	0.3897	0.3791	0.5041	83.95	83.46
0.4789	0.3993	0.3930	0.5414	82.53	82.23
0.0959	0.4984	0.1556	0.6666	86.29	86.38
0.1934	0.5010	0.2470	0.6228	84.18	83.96
0.3099	0.4949	0.3135	0.6009	82.55	82.28
0.4006	0.4991	0.3385	0.6149	81.32	81.10
0.0954	0.6042	0.1347	0.7448	83.97	84.08
0.2124	0.5908	0.2339	0.6877	82.05	81.93
0.4614	0.4118	0.3870	0.5465	82.46	80.23
0.1021	0.6959	0.1266	0.7982	81.94	81.99
0.1952	0.7051	0.1955	0.7680	80.14	80.11
0.0757	0.8162	0.0865	0.8764	80.15	80.25
0.1805	0.7530	0.1768	0.7997	79.49	79.49
0.0526	0.8987	0.0577	0.9264	79.09	79.19

a Predicted using NRTL equation.
b Measured.

Table VII.   Vapor–Liquid Equilibrium Data at 760 mm Hg
Water (1)–Ethanol (2)-3-Methyl-1-Butanol (3)

x_1	x_2	$y_1{}^a$	$y_2{}^a$	$t\,°C{}^b$	$t\,°C{}^b$
0.7422	0.0101	0.8790	0.0198	95.08	94.37
0.4982	0.0127	0.8318	0.0266	97.93	94.67
0.3477	0.0120	0.7503	0.0311	103.20	99.58
0.7248	0.0303	0.8455	0.0589	94.46	93.57
0.2944	0.0263	0.6809	0.0729	104.88	100.44
0.7784	0.0269	0.8464	0.0565	94.56	93.78
0.8878	0.0094	0.8412	0.0277	95.22	95.40
0.0344	0.0241	0.8492	0.0456	95.14	94.13
0.4465	0.0384	0.7685	0.0826	98.26	95.68
0.6338	0.1773	0.6234	0.3225	89.45	89.41
0.5055	0.2112	0.5744	0.3604	89.97	89.71
0.2774	0.1984	0.4574	0.4082	96.20	92.15
0.2087	0.1867	0.3944	0.4306	99.46	93.92
0.3781	0.3232	0.4331	0.5084	88.31	88.31
0.6071	0.2999	0.4801	0.4971	84.75	86.25
0.1377	0.3002	0.2369	0.6182	96.57	91.73
0.1984	0.3953	0.2684	0.6495	90.32	88.62
0.2802	0.4149	0.3265	0.6180	87.35	87.39
0.4460	0.3727	0.4225	0.5431	85.22	86.62
0.1335	0.4835	0.1774	0.7491	89.05	87.69
0.1857	0.5114	0.2212	0.7262	86.56	86.65
0.3912	0.5172	0.3319	0.6538	81.75	84.07
0.1047	0.6257	0.1248	0.8307	85.20	85.37
0.1939	0.6103	0.2054	0.7648	83.33	84.63
0.2963	0.5946	0.2709	0.7134	81.50	83.62
0.1112	0.6845	0.1247	0.8441	83.31	84.20
0.1353	0.7158	0.1428	0.8359	81.85	83.40
0.2135	0.6820	0.2050	0.7806	83.94	82.97
0.0453	0.8104	0.0511	0.9280	81.67	82.76
0.1022	0.8118	0.1059	0.8824	80.21	82.00
0.1547	0.7925	0.1498	0.8434	79.49	81.51
0.0312	0.8920	0.0343	0.9551	80.02	80.09
0.0499	0.8998	0.0532	0.9402	79.38	79.45
0.0680	0.8989	0.0706	0.9252	78.96	78.99

[a] Predicted using NRTL equation.
[b] Measured.

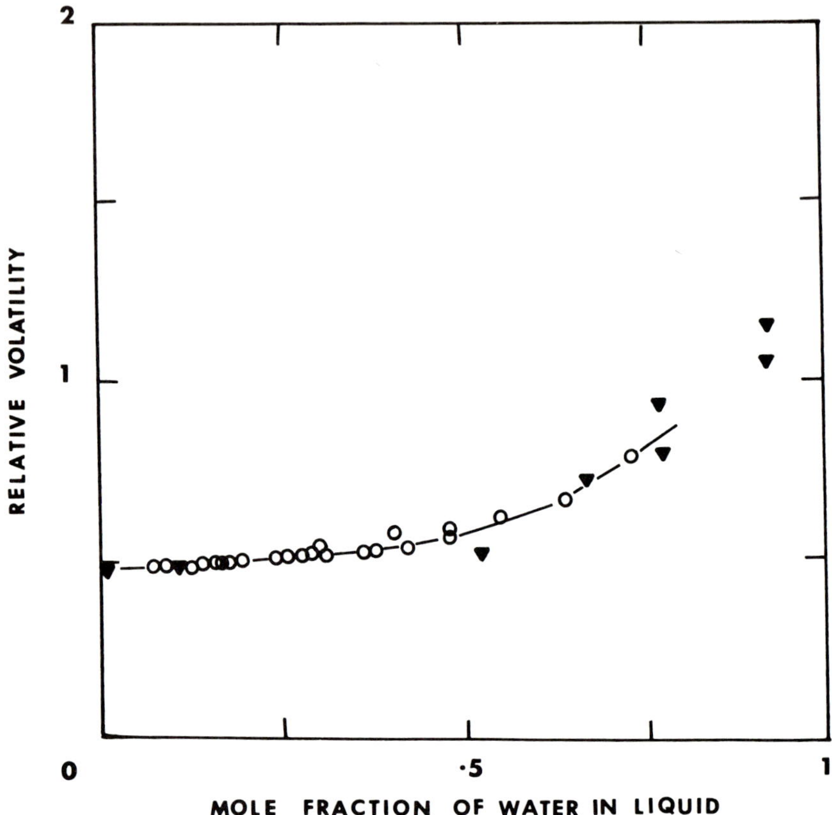

Figure 5.   Comparison of calculated and experimental volatilities of 1-propanol relative to ethanol in presence of water

○ Indirectly measured, present work
▼ Directly measured, Carlson et al. (14)

Conclusion

The non-random, two-liquid (*NRTL*) equation proposed by Renon and Prausnitz (*8*) seems to predict successfully multicomponent (ternary) mixtures of alcohols and water. The alcohols studied in this work ethanol, 1-propanol, 2-methyl-1-propanol, and 3-methyl-1-butanol, which occur from the fermentation of sugar solutions, show highly non-ideal behavior in aqueous solutions and present a severe test of the effectiveness of any prediction method.

The success of the NRTL equation in undergoing this test would suggest that it will be a powerful tool in the design of processes involving azeotropic or extractive distillation. The effect of the addition of a third component to a difficult to separate binary mixture can be predicted with a degree of confidence, certainly for alcohol–water mixtures. Only equilibrium data for the binary components of the system are necessary, and this work shows that even for systems of limited liquid-phase miscibility, the NRTL equation can be used to extract the necessary information from measurements of boiling point, liquid composition, and pressure alone.

Literature Cited

1. Prausnitz, J. M., Eckert, C. A., Orye, R. V., O'Connell, J. P., "Computer Calculations for Multicomponent Vapor–Liquid Equilibria," p. 14, Prentice Hall, New Jersey, 1967.
2. Hala, E., Pick, J., Fried, V., Vilim, O., "Vapor–Liquid Equilibrium," p. 33, Pergamon, London, 1967.
3. Wohl, K., *Trans. Amer. Inst. Chem. Eng.* (1946) **42**, 215.
4. Cukor, P. M., Prausnitz, J. M., Int. Symp. "Distillation," p. 73, Inst. Chem. Eng., London (Sept. 9, 1969).
5. Wilson, G. M., *J. Amer. Chem. Soc.* (1964) **86**, 127.
6. Garrett, G. R., VanWinkle, Matthew, *J. Chem. Eng. Data* (1969) **14**, 302.
7. Gurukul, S. M. K. A., Raju, B. N., *J. Chem. Eng. Data* (1966) **11**, 501.
8. Renon, H., Prausnitz, J. M., *A.I.Ch.E. J.* (1968) **14**, 135.
9. Ellis, S. R. M., Garbett, R. D., *Ind. Eng. Chem.* (1960) **52**, 385.
10. Othmer, D. F., Gilmont, R., Conti, J. J., *Ind. Eng. Chem.* (1960) **52**, 625.
11. Rieder, R. M., Thompson, A. R., *Ind. Eng. Chem.* (1949) **41**, 2905.
12. Murti, P. S., VanWinkle, Matthew, *Ind. Eng. Chem., J. Chem. Eng. Data* (1958) **3**, 72.
13. Timmermans, J., "The Physico Chemical Constants of Binary Systems," Vol. 4, p. 237, Interscience, New York (1960).
14. Carlson, C. S., Smith, P. V., Jr., Morrell, C. E., *Ind. Eng. Chem.* (1954) **46**, 350.
15. Gadwa, T. W., Chemical Engineering Thesis, M.I.T., 1936.
16. Gay, L., *Chim. et Ind.* (1927) **18**, 187.

7

Demulsification of Crude Oils

Use of Azeotropic Distillation

LESLIE L. BALASSA and DONALD F. OTHMER

Slate Hill, N. Y. 10973 and Polytechnic Institute, Brooklyn, N. Y. 11201

Water and often fine sand and silt are held in various crude oils in permanent emulsions. Particularly crudes obtained by secondary methods and those from tar sands where water or steam are used contain water and mineral matter emulsified therein by the surface forces on small particles and drops. Azeotropic distillation removes the relatively small amount of water, using the solvent as an entrainer which dilutes the crude. This allows: the mineral matter to be separated easily without using centrifuges with their substantial cost and wear, free of organic material, so it may be discarded without hazards of fire or odors; the bitumen to be recovered for such use or cracked to give volatile fractions and coked to an ash-free coke; the water to be obtained as distilled water for reuse.

Petroleum crudes produced by water flooding, hot water displacement, pressure steam, or steam injection usually are emulsions, either water-in-oil or oil-in-water, and are frequently a combination of both. Emulsions of these high viscosity oils often cannot be broken and dehydrated by conventional methods.

An even more difficult processing condition arises with heavy bituminous oils which always carry much sand, clay, and silt of coarse and small particle sizes which stabilize the oil–water emulsions even more. The bituminous oils have specific gravities of 0.9–1.4 and have high viscosities; thus they cannot be separated from the water or solids present by settling or by using the most efficient centrifuges.

Diluting these emulsions of heavy oils with light solvents—*e.g.*, kerosene, solvent naphtha, benzene, etc.—reduces the specific gravity of the oil phase of the emulsions below that of water and lowers the viscosity so that some of the water and mineral matters usually can be removed by sedimentation, centrifuge, or hydro-cyclone.

Addition of a low viscosity hydrocarbon solvent often extracts the oil from the water; the extract layer of solvent and solute separates from the water. The large amount of solvent needed to separate emulsions of water in a viscous heavy oil is uneconomic because of the dilute solution needed to obtain a continuous water phase. Addition of solvent, possibly up to an equal amount, is reasonable and is desirable to reduce the viscosity sufficiently to pump and transport the heavy oil. A cheap aliphatic solvent— e.g., kerosene—is preferable, but bituminous oil fractions are much more soluble in aromatic solvents, particularly at temperatures near the ambient. However, the water and solid particles are not at acceptable limits even after much dilution, especially in the presence of fine particles as in some crudes from California and Venezuela and particularly from tar sands as those in Athabasca (Alberta, Canada).

Processing oil emulsions from tar sands is difficult with the oil and the aqueous phase. The oil phase carries much clay and silt (sand) of small particle size which are suspended and do not settle out even on prolonged storage. The surface or molecular forces between viscous oils and such fine particles are more important in determining the latter's motions, or lack of motion, than the mechanical forces resulting from differences in specific gravity.

Some particles in the aqueous phase are wet by oil instead of by water, and these oil-coated particles give an unusually stable suspension for about the same reason. This oil in the oil-wet mineral matter, suspended in the aqueous phase, makes it unsuitable for recycling in the processing operation or discharging back into surface waters. Also, the mineral sludge which is separated from water still contains a substantial percentage of oil; it cannot be disposed of even by returning it to the place where it was mined or produced. Fires have occurred from spontaneous combustion resulting from this sludge of fine particles and oil.

Prior processes proposed to demulsify it are unsatisfactory because so much oil is always lost in the aqueous phase or in the dewatered sludge. Also, the content of water and minerals in the oil separated by conventional processes is usually above acceptable limits for pipeline transportation or for refining purposes.

Financial losses are experienced in oil wasted, in equipment and capital charges of worn equipment in plants, and in land value of disposal ponds. Tremendous disposal ponds of discarded emulsions in Venezuela and elsewhere take up available land. In separating emulsions from tar sands, the extremely abrasive silt has ruined expensive centrifuges and makes using them impractical.

Azeotropic Distillation

The water content of an emulsion is removed by distillation, however, direct and simple distillation presents several practical problems. In the presence of a solvent–diluent after preliminary separation of much of the water as a continuous phase, the balance is removed by azeotropic distillation.

For many years water has been separated from many liquids by azeotropic distillation. Water is substantially insoluble not only in the oils but also in the diluents or solvents. Thus, the vapor pressures of the water and diluent are additive as in the familiar steam distillations. A heterogeneous azeotrope is formed; this always boils below the boiling point of water because pressure must be reduced for water to boil at the vapor pressure of the hydrocarbon.

The principles of azeotropic distillation have often been described (1, 2, 3, 4, 5, 6, 7), and applying them gives a simple method of separating water from its oil emulsions. The low-boiling constituents of an oil—or the diluent used—would be the entrainer (withdrawing agent) which forms the heterogeneous azeotrope or steam distillation with the water.

Because of nonequilibrium boiling conditions in a simple distillation, the vapors may not contain the true azeotrope, and the heat cost may be too high. Therefore a column is still used to rectify the exact azeotrope at the head of the column; however, only a few trays are required.

The azeotrope contains the lower hydrocarbons of the diluent. If a wide-cut fraction is used, the more volatile ones come to the top of the column with the water.

At any temperature the vapor pressure of water plus that of the entrainer, or the effective vapor pressure of the mixture of liquids operating as the entrainer, gives the azeotrope's vapor pressure. The temperature where this summation curve crosses the atmospheric line, or other operating pressure of the distillation, is the azeotropic boiling point. A close-cut fraction or a single more or less pure compound as a diluent and azeotropic withdrawing agent is preferable, although not necessary. If the mixture loses some of its more volatile components at the head of the column over a period of time, the azeotropic boiling point will gradually rise.

The condensate has two liquid phases. It runs from the condenser to a separator or decanter where the water layer is removed for discard and the solvent layer is returned, usually as reflux to the column. This reflux of "all or part" (the solvent layer) of the condensate after decantation, rather than "part of all," was developed in 1927 (2) for acetic acid dehydration with an added solvent as entrainer and for butanol dehydration using butanol itself as the entrainer.

Separating water from an oil emulsion is best done by an entrainer added as a diluent to the oil. For example, the diluent added to the oil emulsion is a naphtha fraction having an effective vapor pressure equal to that of octane. This naphtha is added to the oil, and as much water as possible is separated; the oil emulsion layer which is not broken contains the added naphtha.

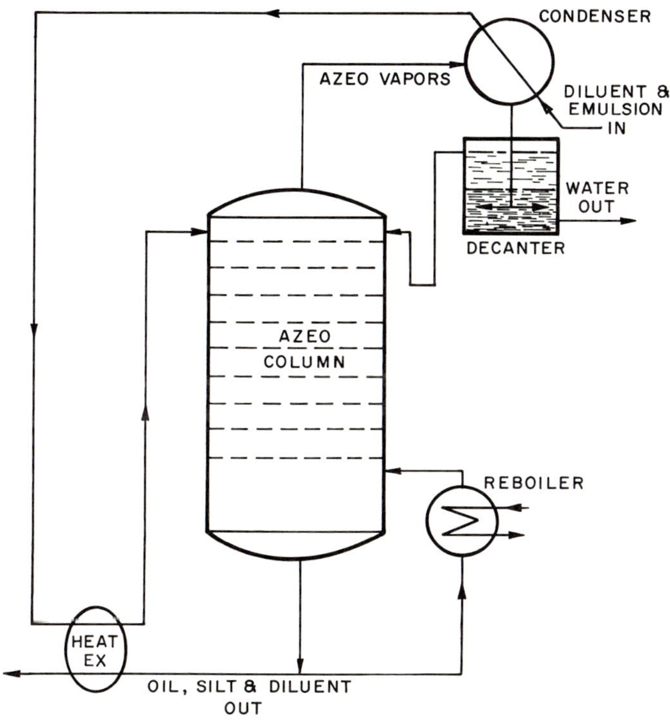

Figure 1. Flow sheet for removing emulsified water from crude oil and diluent using azeotropic distillation with fixed amount of entrainer

Figure 1 indicates one operable flow sheet when this oil emulsion containing the naphtha will have a sufficiently low viscosity to be pumped through a tubular condenser and then through a tubular bottoms cooler for heat interchanging and recovery. It is then pumped to an upper plate of a column still. This might have 10–15 trays designed to allow ready passage downward of any silt. The column is thus self-cleaning as much as possible, but provisions are also made for opening to clean mechanically, if necessary.

Table I gives several azeotropes of water with hydrocarbons and butanol, used as entrainers. Assuming the entrainer–diluent has the prop-

Table I.　Azeotropes of Water and Entrainers

	Temperature, °C (1 atm)		Composition % by Weight			Separated Layers	
Compound	Boiling Point	Azeo. Temp.	Azeo. Vapors	Upper Layers	Lower Layers	Volume, %	
Toluene	110.6		79.8	99.9	0.1	82	Up
Water	100	85	20.2	0.1	99.9	18	Low
m-Xylene	139.1		60	99.95	0.05	63.4	Up
Water	100	94.5	40	0.05	99.95	36.6	Low
n-Octane	125.7		74.5	99.98	0.02	80	Up
Water	100	89.6	25.5	0.02	99.98	20	Low
Butanol	117.7		55.5	77.5	8.0	71.5	Up
Water	100	93	45.5	22.5	92.0	28.5	Low

erties of octane, the column has a top vapor temperature of 89.6°C. These vapors are condensed in preheating the feed and in another water-cooled condenser if needed. The condensate flows to a decanter which continuously separates 80% by volume as the diluent–entrainer layer and 20% by volume of a water layer. The amount of each component dissolved in the other layer is so small that it is disregarded; thus the water layer flows to waste. The entrainer layer is returned to the top of the column as reflux to withdraw more water, and the dry oil with sediment passes out the bottom and through a bottoms exchanger. The silt now settles and separates relatively easily from the oil which is decanted. The silt is washed with the solvent–diluent which is then reused with a following oil emulsion and then steamed to recover the naphtha.

In this flow sheet the solvent–diluent–entrainer passes through the system and out with the oil for transport or refining—a first step which may recover naphtha for reuse. However, in the cycle at the head of the azeotropic column with the condenser and the decanter, fractionating light-ends from the naphtha passing through with the oil occurs to give the azeotrope with water which has a composition depending on the effective vapor pressure of the mixture of hydrocarbons which stabilizes there as time passes. This may have a considerably lower boiling point than the naphtha fraction, and the light-ends congregate and become the entrainer. Some of this may be removed from the system by withdrawing from the reflux stream to the column. If there are so many low ends that the azeotropic boiling point goes down, a naphtha fraction of somewhat higher boiling range is used as the diluent.

Actually this indicates an operation comparable with the dehydration of many other liquids with a separate entrainer. Thus, if no diluent is necessary to reduce the viscosity of the oil so that it may be handled and no diluent is used to give a previous partial demulsification, enough entrainer could be selected and supplied to the azeotropic system to charge the upper part of the column, the condenser, decanter, and connections. The added entrainer would then withdraw water from the oil emulsion fed into and out of the column, and the entrainer would then act like a mechanical part of the system.

Table I shows that, as the boiling point of the hydrocarbon used as the entrainer increases so does that of the azeotrope with water and the percent of water therein. A high percentage of water in the azeotrope is desired for the heat required for the distillation, which is mainly that of the latent heat of the water plus that of the entrainer. Sufficient entrainer should be available in the azeotrope for reflux to the column although this requirement is not large. Also, the solubility or dilution effect is better with lower-boiling hydrocarbons. Thus there are several factors to be balanced in choosing the azeotrope. The effect of relative boiling points, vapor pressures, and amounts of different entrainers in their azeotropes with water has been discussed as affecting the choice of entrainers for separating water from acetic acid (5). However, that represents a much more difficult selection because there the quantity of reflux is important and also the solvent characteristics of the entrainer for the acetic acid also control the choice.

However, the optimum azeotropic entrainer for water from an oil emulsion is partially selected according to those principles. The highest boiling liquids obviously carry more water for a given heat input. A selected and stable temperature at the top of the azeo column is necessary for optimum operation, and this might seem to be secured best by a pure aromatic. Alternately, a pure aliphatic or a close-cut naphtha fraction might be obtained and maintained in the azeotropic column. The use of a pure compound is not advantageous if a close-cut naphtha fraction is used as an entrainer in this continuous operation because the losses and make-up of such entrainer in a column are so small; thus, the effective azeotropic boiling point remains constant.

The entrainer should be a hydrocarbon which has a lower boiling point than the light ends, whatever the feedstock of oil emulsion; otherwise light ends continually fractionate into the azeotrope and have to be removed. In other systems involving azeotropic withdrawing agents with a mixture of various volatilities, a stable entrainer is developed and maintained at the desired boiling point by removing periodically some of the entrainer to keep its effective boiling point sufficiently high. Sometimes small heads columns have been incorporated to do this continuously.

Laboratory Testing

Having considered a basic flow sheet and the elementary principles of azeotropic distillation as they may be used, we considered testing emulsions in the laboratory prior to process design.

The first step in testing the material for suitability of the demulsifying, dehydrating process is to dilute the crude oil with a solvent which is used by itself or mixed with another in azeotropic dehydration of the emulsion. The minimum amount of solvent which is sufficient for the first step is that which cuts the viscosity of the crude enough to allow azeotropic distillation without excessive foaming. This may require about 40–60 volumes solvent per 100 volumes of crude, but this ratio of solvent, however, may not be sufficient to reduce the gravity of the crude below that of water to allow preliminary decantation of some of the water.

To achieve this, a volume of solvent about equal to that of the crude may have to be used (sometimes an even higher ratio of solvent). By diluting the crude first with toluene up to a volume of 20% of the crude and continuing the dilution with a light gasoline fraction in the range of hexane, octane, or higher, the gravity is lowered with less total solvent. Also dilution with a naphtha fraction alone may suffice at 80°C. Each crude has to be separately evaluated based on its properties and water content. If the water in the permanent emulsion is low, it may not be worthwhile to add sufficient solvent to separate a water layer.

The water in the crude which is not in a permanent emulsion is determined by diluting the crude with a mixture of toluene and a naphtha fraction; much of the water together with the water-set inorganic matter then settles out in a separatory funnel. If a centrifuge is used, the high gravity oil-wet inorganic matter separates with the water carrying with it a substantial amount of oil. Thus, simple gravity separation is preferable.

The oil diluted with the solvent *only* may be distilled in a glass flask, fitted with a relatively simple laboratory column. Boiling in the flask is accomplished without bumping if an internal electric heater which allows little superheat is used. The azeotropic distillation brings over vapors which are condensed. Condensate is separated in a continuous glass decanter which returns the hydrocarbon layer to the column and discharges the water layer. When the water content of the solution is reduced to below 0.1–0.2%, no water is visible in the condensate; the temperature at the head of the column rises to the boiling point of the entrainer itself, and the dehydration is complete. The total water separated is measured. This volume with the water which has been separated by decantation after dilution and before distillation represents the original amount of water present.

Batch azeotropic distillation is also accomplished in the laboratory with a simple flask, condenser, and receiver without a column, continuous decanter, and continuous reflux, but it takes much longer and is not comparable to a plant operation, which is developed from such laboratory testing.

The oil-wet sludge is removed from the dehydrated oil solution in the flask by settling and decanting or centrifuging. It is washed with solvent to free it of oil, dried, and weighed. The wash solution is combined with the dehydrated oil solution which contains other solvent and the separate entrainer, if one was used. Solvent is stripped from the solution by distillation to determine the available oil of the crude which remains.

A small amount of additional inorganic matter may settle out of crude after a few days storage. This is an extremely small particle size silt which is usually less than 0.05% of the oil. It might be removed by a more efficient, higher speed, centrifuge than usually available. However, such high speed centrifuges might be badly abraded by the fine silt and would be too expensive to use in actual practice. One or two days settling at 120°C for example, is a better test method and is a better practice in production if the necessary storage facilities are available. Additives to flocculate the fine silt might also be used.

Modified Azeotropic Distillation

Continuous distillation always gives a better, more uniform product at a lower heat cost and usually a lower plant cost. A continuous operation is essential in azeotropic distillation when an entrainer is added, or it would necessarily have to be fractionated off to reuse it after each batch.

Several variations of the flow sheet for azeotropic distillation are possible, each having a continuous decanter which discharges pure water (less than 0.1% dissolved hydrocarbon or aromatics and less than 0.01% for aliphatics). Figure 1 is the simplest flow sheet. The entrainer selected is charged to the azeotropic column and remains substantially there, removing water continuously but being almost unchanged if it has a lower boiling point than the light ends of the feedstock. The reboiler may be heated by other ways than by the steam shown in Figure 1.

Figure 2 shows a continuous azeotropic column using a fixed amount of entrainer which remains in the unit. Since reflux is largely supplied by feed of the emulsion near the top of the column, the entrainer from the decanter passes to a reboiler and is fed back to the tower as vapors. This gives a more nearly counter-current action of the azeotropic distilling operation, and a lesser heat input required into the viscous oil at the base of the column, usually with more or less silt in suspension while

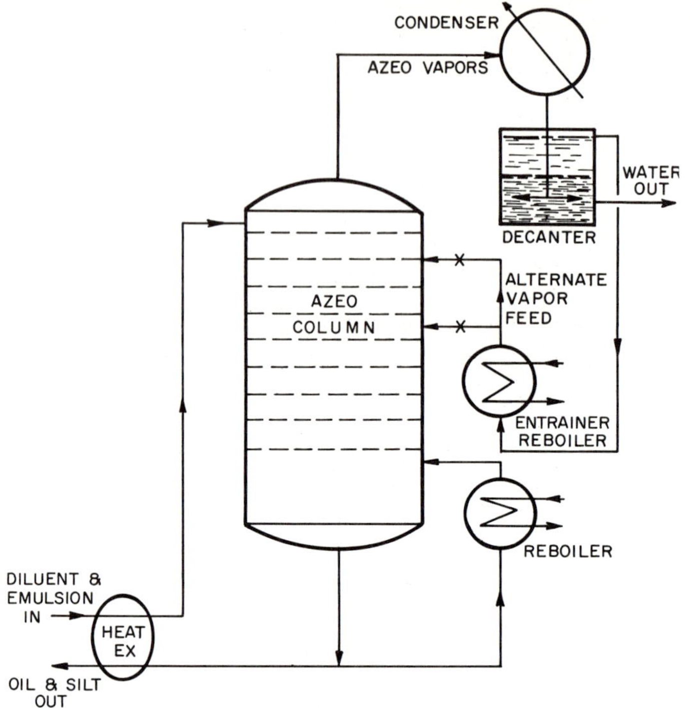

*Figure 2.   Flow sheet for removing emulsified water by azeo-
tropic distillation using a vapor feed of the reflux of a fixed
amount of entrainer*

the balance of the heat requirements for the azeotropic distillation would
be supplied to the thin, pure, entrainer in a separate reboiler.

Figure 3 utilizes the diluting of the oil emulsion with the entrainer
coming from the decanter. This occurs at or near the azeotropic boiling
point. This mixer dissolves the oil in the emulsion and partially breaks
it with some of the water and silt being decanted off of the feed stream
of permanent emulsion and entrainer-solvent going to the top of the
column. More entrainer must be used in this system to supply that in
the mixer and the decanter; however, it is mixed with the oil passing
through continuously.

Figure 4 is a modification of Figure 3 where the function of the mixer
in dissolving the entrainer and the feed of oil emulsion and the function of
the decanter in separating the water layer formed is taken over by an extractor. It is one of the several mechanically agitated types which washes
or extracts the oil out of the emulsion and precipitates or discharges as a
raffinate layer the water along with most of the silt. The remaining permanent emulsion oil layer carried by the dissolving entrainer solvent goes
to the top of the column.

The bottom of Figure 4 indicates one system for the handling of the crude with silt from the bottom of the column before, after, or without a heat exchanger to recover the sensible heat of the bottoms from this still. A continuous thickener, of the usual rotating type with hoes, thickens the suspended silt into an oil-mud which is removed, washed, and steamed before discard. The solvent recovered from this washing of mud goes back to the feed dissolution. The clear crude kerosene solution, now free of water and silt, has kerosene removed by distillation, or it is pumped to the refinery. Often where the crude does not contain too much water in a permanent emulsion or is not too difficult to pump, it would not require the initial dilution.

Other variations of flows are possible; in each case if more solvent-entrainer is added to the emulsion in advance, it is recovered by drawing off a corresponding percentage of the entrainer layer which discharges from the decanter and recycling it back to solution tank where it is added to the optimum proportional amount of feed emulsion. Thus, if kerosene and an aromatic solvent—*e.g.*, toluene or xylene—are used in dissolution of the emulsion, the aromatic chosen as the entrainer is continuously

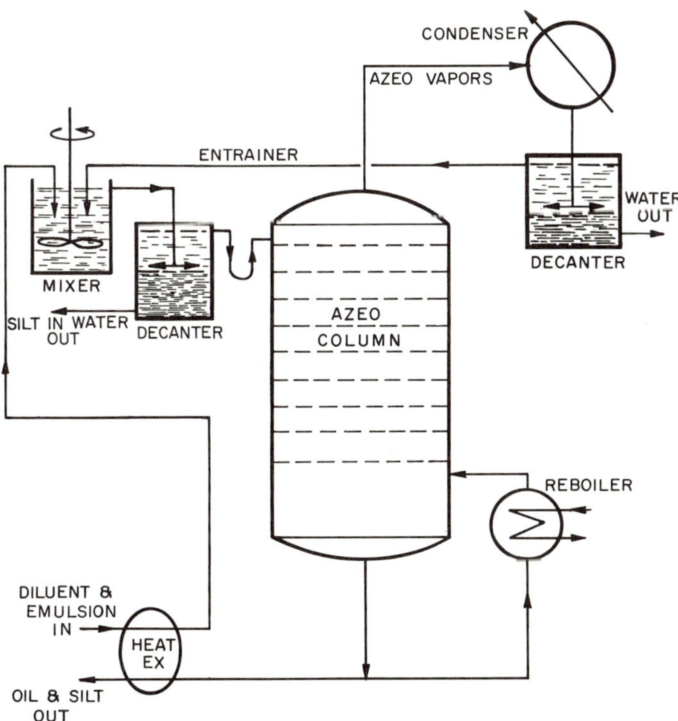

Figure 3.   Flow sheet using entrainer as diluent with premixer and predecanter for separating some of the silt and water

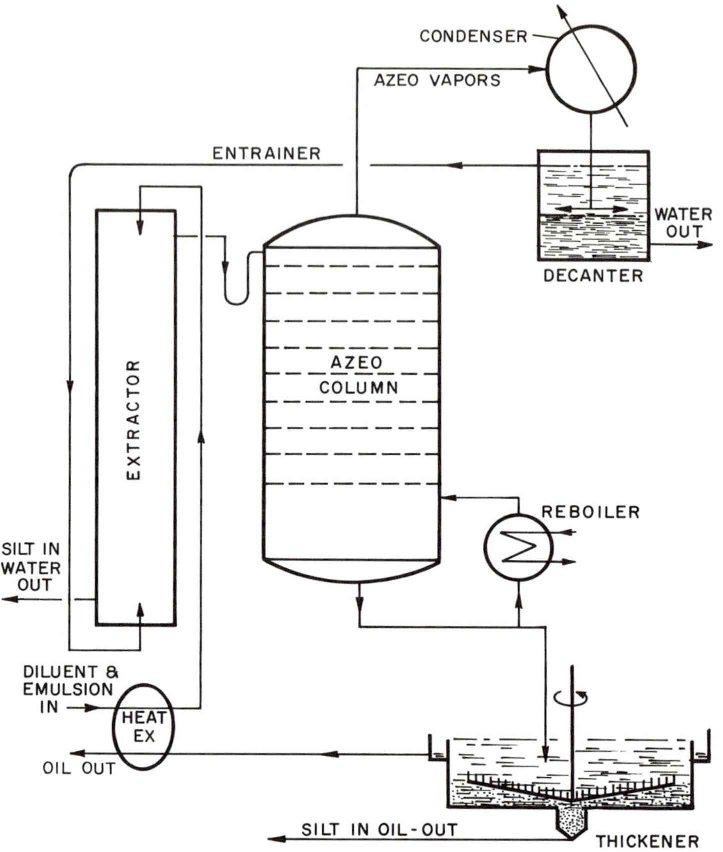

Figure 4.   Flow sheet using entrainer as diluent solvent in an extractor used to extract oil from an emulsion with water and to remove a raffinate layer of silt and water (with removal of final silt from the bottoms stream by a thickener, either before or after a heat exchanger)

separated in the amount of its arrival in the column and recycled back for continuous dissolution in the mixer. This is controlled by observing the temperatures at several midsection plates, the same as the amount of butyl acetate in the column is controlled in acetic acid dehydration (5). The higher boiling kerosene is distilled away from the crude in a separate column, or it may remain to thin the crude in its transport to the refinery.

Comparison of Azeotropic Demulsification with GCOS Process

To exemplify the problems of demulsification of oil, some steps in the recovery of bituminous oil from tar sands are considered. The Great Canadian Oil Sands, Ltd. (GCOS) Process has been described in various publications (*e.g.*, *8*), and because of the major problems of separating water and abrasive minerals from the crude, operational losses of many millions of dollars have resulted.

Mining—overburden, removal, and mining of tar sands

Transport—tar sands conveyed, stored, and loaded in extractors

Primary Extraction. This is accomplished with steam and hot water in rotating conditioning drums at about 190°F. The total mass is piped into a vertical separation cell where—(a) the crude bitumen, as a froth, rises to the surface and is removed; (b) a bottom layer containing mainly sand, clay, and water with not more than about 2% bitumen is piped to the tailing pond; (c) a "middlings" layer without sharp dividing lines between the froth above or the sand and water below. This is a tenacious emulsion of bitumen in water, stabilized by a substantial amount of sand and clay—mostly oil-wet. Most of the bitumen is removed in scavenger cells by air-frothing. The sand, clay, and water and some unrecoverable bitumen is pumped to the tailings pond. Bitumen recovery is not more than 90%, thus the tailings carry off at least 10% of that originally present.

Final Extraction. The bitumen from the froth, containing substantial quantities of sand, clay, and water, is diluted with naphtha to reduce its viscosity so it can be pumped readily. It is first pumped to 14 scroll-type centrifuges to remove large mineral particles and then to 26 nozzle-type centrifuges to remove most of the remaining minerals and water. Abrasion in the expensive centrifuges has been a major operational charge. The diluted bitumen still contains significant quantities of water and hydrophilic sand and clay.

Cracking and Coking. The dilute bitumen is pumped into coker drums, where it is cracked to yield gas and crude oil overhead, which goes to the refinery. Residual coke contains all of the residual sand and clay which could not be removed in the final extraction, and therefore it is used only as a fuel for the boilers.

In the azeotropic system (*1*), the mining and transport steps are the same, also the cracking and coking step, except that it gives a much improved coke which is used for more valuable products than as a high ash fuel.

In the primary extraction, however, a hydrocarbon solvent is added. This allows a relatively sharp separation between the "middlings" and the aqueous bottom layer. A fraction with boiling range of octane is suitable, since it then becomes the azeotropic entrainer for the water. An aromatic solvent—*e.g.*, toluene—might be better, but it may require another separation later.

In the final extraction because of solvent addition in the primary extraction, the mineral matter readily separates from the bottom aqueous layer instead of requiring batteries of expensive centrifuges with considerable damage resulting from abrasion of the fine sand. A suitable settling aid assists this, and the wet sediment, almost free of bitumen, is used as fill. The water contains only a small amount of dissolved solvent which is recovered by stripping, or wasted, and the water itself is reused or discarded to surface waters as it is environmentally acceptable.

The top bitumen layer and the "middlings" layer are combined and are pumped to an azeotropic distillation system, as diagrammed in Figures 1, 2, 3, and 4. The choice of flow sheet depends on the relative amounts of water remaining and the amounts and characteristics of the mineral matter. The systems of Figures 3 and 4 remove more water and silt before the azeotropic distillation, thus saving heat. Using the system of Figure 4 instead of the thickener, a simple storage tank allowing two days residence for settling out all silt, including colloidal clay which passes through the column, may be used after the heat exchanger.

If a naphtha fraction has been used in the dilution and as the entrainer, it is left in as a diluent for reducing the viscosity in pumping the oil to the refinery. Alternatively, some or all is removed as a slip stream from the reflux going to the top of the azeotropic column. If toluene or other aromatic solvent is used, it would be so removed or removed in a separate distillation for recycle.

Oil-wet materials, sand, and clay, separated from either oil or water layers, are washed with the solvent or diluent until they are free of bitumen and the residual solvent is stripped from the mineral matter with steam. The mineral matter is clean and is sent to waste or used as fill without danger of spontaneous combustion, or it is used in cement manufacture. The aqueous phases condensed from such stripping and from the decanter of the azeotropic system has so little solvent, in hundredths of a percent, that it is neglected. It evaporates readily in open storage. This distilled water is used for any suitable purpose.

Recovery of the bitumen by this system has been almost 98% compared with the losses in the GCOS system, and the solvent losses are low.

The major advantage of this system is elimination of the 14-scroll type centrifuges and 26-nozzle type machines used in the GCOS plant which have had excessive replacement, maintenance, and repair costs because of the abrasive action of the fine solids on these high speed, precision machines.

The bitumen obtained is the unmodified native bitumen with a substantial percentage of high melting, aliphatic soluble components. These are separated from the low melting components by solvent extraction or solvent precipitation. The high melting components are utilized in protective coatings for metals or in heat resistant road surface compositions.

If coke is obtained from this process, it is free of mineral matter and is used for the same uses as other high grade petroleum cokes—*e.g.*, in electrodes or activated carbon, as well as in metallurgical uses where the high ash content resulting from the residual minerals would prevent that from the GCOS system being used.

Another advantage is that little water is required in the azeotropic process since most of the water is recycled and that which is not recycled is immediately passed to surface waters without environmental damage. Also, removing all organics from the mineral matters means that these can be used as fill or otherwise without fire hazard, odors, or other environmental problems caused by microbiological attacks on any residual bitumen left on the minerals as in the GCOS process.

Literature Cited

1. Balassa, L. L., **U.S. Patent 3,468,789** (Sept. 23, 1969).
2. Clarke, H. T., Othmer, D. F., **U.S. Patent 1,804,745** (May 12, 1931).
3. Othmer, D. F., "Encyclopedia of Chemical Technology," 2nd ed., Vol. 2, p. 839, 1963.
4. Othmer, D. F., **U.S. Patent 1,917,391** (July 11, 1933).
5. Othmer, D. F., *Chem. & Met. Eng.* (1941) **48**, 91.
6. Othmer, D. F., *Chem. Eng. Progr.* (1963) **59**, 6, 67.
7. Othmer, D. F., TenEyck, E. H., *Ind. Eng. Chem.* (1949) **41**, 2897.
8. "Our Sun," Sun Oil Co., House Publication (Autumn, 1967).

RECEIVED November 24, 1970.

8

Distillation Calculations with Nonideal Mixtures

JOSEPH A. BRUNO, JOHN L. YANOSIK,[a] and JOHN W. TIERNEY

Chemical Engineering Department, University of Pittsburgh, Pittsburgh, Pa. 15213

A new iteration sequence is presented for solving distillation problems with composition dependent equilibrium and enthalpy relations. For a steady state, non-reacting system with m components and n stages, the procedure requires simultaneous iteration of n(m + 1) variables. These are the vapor flow rates, the stage temperatures, and all but one of the liquid compositions. The basic equations for an equilibrium stage system are presented using matrix notation. The calculation sequence is outlined, and a correction algorithm based on Newton's method is derived. This requires the calculation of the Jacobian matrix of partial derivatives, and an analytical method for obtaining these derivatives by vector differentiation of the system equations is presented. This method is much simpler than those used previously. Modification of the iteration process to hold selected vapor flows constant is described, and a method of obtaining starting values for the first iteration is presented. Results obtained from solution of a sample extractive distillation problem are presented. Quadratic convergence is obtained near the solution, indicating that the equations derived for the Jacobian matrix are correct.

The mathematical model for a steady state equilibrium stage separation process consists of a large set of simultaneous nonlinear equations which must be solved to determine the phase flow rates, the stage temperatures, and the phase composition. A matrix notation was previously presented (1, 2) which permits writing the equations in a concise form

[a] Present address: AMOCO Production Co., Tulsa, Okla.

and provides for any interstage flow pattern. It was also shown that these equations can be analytically differentiated to obtain iterative algorithms with quadratic convergence rates near the solution. For the case where the equilibrium ratios are functions only of stage temperatures and not of compositions, it was shown that quadratic convergence can be obtained by simultaneous iteration of only the stage temperatures and the vapor flow rates. All other variables can be obtained by solving nothing more complicated than sets of simultaneous linear equations. Once a set of temperatures and vapor flows are assumed, the equations become linear in the remaining variables. Thus, for a system with n stages and m components, it is only necessary to iterate on $2n$ variables rather than the complete set of $n(2m + 3)$ unknowns.

If the equilibrium ratios are functions of phase compositions as occurs in liquid extraction or extractive distillation, it is necessary to include more variables in the iterative process. It was later shown (3) that for liquid extraction problems with known stage temperatures, the minimum number of iteration variables for quadratic convergence is nm, the n vapor flow rates, and $n(m - 1)$ of the phase compositions. The total number of variables is $n(2m + 2)$ because the temperatures are known. The iteration sequence is completely different for this case as compared with the previous case with composition independent equilibrium ratios.

Developed here is a correction process with quadratic convergence near the solution for problems in which the equilibrium ratios are composition dependent and in which the stage temperatures are not fixed but must be determined. It is necessary to introduce the energy balance equations to give the additional equations needed. The derivation follows the general lines of that for the liquid extraction problem, but the extension is not trivial. The method requires the simultaneous correction of $n(m + 1)$ variables. We will also present a simplified method of analytically differentiating the matrix equations which greatly reduces the work necessary to derive a correction algorithm.

In related investigations Roche (4) has demonstrated quadratic convergence for composition dependent liquid extraction problems at constant temperature. He essentially iterates on all $n(2m + 2)$ variables. Nelson (5) has used the matrix notation of References 1 and 2 to investigate systems where chemical reaction occurs in the stages.

Equations for an Equilibrium Separation System

The equations describing a steady-state equilibrium stage system without chemical reaction are summarized here. The matrix notation has been previously discussed ($1, 2, 3$), and all symbols are defined below.

The overall material balance equation gives an important relation between the liquid and vapor flow rate vectors, V and L.

$$\underline{B} L + \underline{A} V + \sum_j (F^j) = 0 \tag{1}$$

The matrices A and B are fixed by the interstage flow pattern and together with the feed matrix F are assumed to be given in the problem statement.

The fact that the liquid compositions must sum to a constant (1.0 if mole fractions are used) in each stage is given by:

$$\sum_j (X^j) = U \tag{2}$$

A similar equation can be written for the vapor phase, but it is not independent and can be derived by combining Equations (1), (2), and (3).

A material balance can be written for each component in each stage,

$$\underline{B}\,\underline{L}\,X^j + \underline{A}\,\underline{V}\,Y^j + F^j = 0;\; 1 \le j \le m \tag{3}$$

X^j and Y^j are vectors containing liquid and vapor compositions for component j. The matrices $\underline{L}$ and $\underline{V}$ are diagonal and have the same elements on the diagonal as the vectors L and V.

An energy balance around each stage gives

$$\underline{B}\,\underline{L}\,H + \underline{A}\,\underline{V}\,G + Q + Q_f = 0 \tag{4}$$

H and G are vectors containing the specific enthalpies of liquid and vapor phases in each stage. Q is the vector of stage heat duties, and Q_f is the feed enthalpy vector. Q and Q_f are assumed to be given in the problem statement.

The equilibrium relation between liquid and vapor compositions is given by

$$\underline{\Lambda}^j\,Y^j - \underline{\Gamma}^j\,\underline{K}^j\,X^j = 0;\; 1 \le j \le m \tag{5}$$

Λ^j and Γ^j are the activity coefficient matrices for vapor and liquid phases and are diagonal. For ideal solutions, they become the identity matrix. $\underline{K}^j$ is the fugacity ratio matrix and is also diagonal.

The enthalpies and equilibrium data are physical properties of the mixtures being separated and are assumed to be known explicit functions of compositions and temperatures as follows:

$$H = H(X^2, X^3, .. X^m, T) \tag{6}$$

$$G = G(Y^2, Y^3, .. Y^m, T) \tag{7}$$

$$\underline{\Gamma} = \underline{\Gamma}(X^2, X^3, .. X^m, T) \tag{8}$$

$$\underline{\Lambda} = \underline{\Lambda}(Y^2, Y^3, .. Y^m, T) \tag{9}$$

$$\underline{K} = \underline{K}(T) \tag{10}$$

Each of the above functions is assumed to be continuous and to possess first derivatives with respect to composition and temperature. Also, the composition of component 1 is not to be considered as an independent variable in the development which follows, and this is emphasized by omitting X^1 and Y^1 as arguments in Equations 6–9.

The Calculation Sequence

Equations 1–10 constitute a set of $(5m + 5)$ matrix equations which are to be solved simultaneously to determine $2m$ composition vectors, two flow vectors, a temperature vector, two enthalpy vectors, $2m$ activity coefficient vectors, and m fugacity ratio vectors. The solution must be iterative because the equations are nonlinear. However, there are various methods of organizing the calculations, and one of our primary objects here is to develop an efficient calculation order. At one extreme it would be possible to consider all $5m + 5$ vectors as iteration variables and thus to have a process with $(5m + 5)n$ variables of iteration. It seems obvious that a more efficient method is to reduce the size of the iterative process by eliminating as many of the variables as possible. In practice, it is undesirable actually to eliminate the variables; instead the variables will be divided into two groups. The first group is the variables which will be iterated and will be called the iterated or independent variables; the second group will be called dependent variables. One equation must be used to define each dependent variable, and these equations will be called the defining equations. The remaining equations, equal in number to the independent variables, will be called the error equations. The iteration sequence will then be to assume first a set of values for the independent variables and then to solve the defining equations for the dependent variables. The error equations are then used to correct the independent variables, and the process is repeated.

The number of independent variables should generally be as small as possible. Also, the defining equations should permit simple calculation of the dependent variables, and the correction process itself should be simple and efficient. Here the set of independent variables has been chosen to be as small as possible subject to the limitation that the defining equations remain linear in the dependent variables. The correction algorithm is also linear and is the multivariable form of the Newton–Raphson method.

The set of independent variables which satisfies these requirements is the vapor flow vector V, the liquid phase compositions, X^2 to X^m, and the temperature vector T. The calculation sequence is,

    a. Values are assumed for $(V, X^2, X^3, \ldots X^m, T)$.

    b. The liquid flow vector L is calculated using Equation 1.

    c. Equation 2 is used to calculate X^1.

    d. Equation 3 is used m times to calculate $Y^1, Y^2, \ldots Y^m$.

    e. Equations 6–10 are used to calculate the dependent variables H, G, Λ, Γ, and K. All variables have now been evaluated for the current set of independent variables.

    f. Current values for all variables are substituted into the error equations, which are Equations 4 and 5. If the equations are satisfied, the iterative process is terminated. Otherwise, the independent variables must be corrected, and the calculation repeated from Step b.

The Jacobian Correction Matrix

The only undefined step in the calculation sequence proposed above is the correction of the independent variables in step f. A linear correction process is given by

$$(\underline{J})_v \left\{ (C)_{v+1} - (C)_v \right\} = - (D)_v \tag{11}$$

where C is the direct sum of the independent variables in the order $(V, X^2, X^3, \ldots X^m, T)$, and D is the direct sum of the error vectors, defined as

$$E^k = \underline{\Lambda}^k Y^k - \underline{\Gamma}^k \underline{K}^k X^k; \; 1 \leq k \leq m \tag{12}$$

$$E^{m+1} = \underline{B} \, \underline{L} \, H + \underline{A} \, \underline{V} \, G + Q + Q_f \tag{13}$$

The most rapid convergence of Equation 11 to the solution is obtained when J is the Jacobian matrix, defined as the matrix in which each element is the partial derivative of one of the errors with respect to one of the iteration variables with all other iteration variables held constant. Thus, an estimate of the effect of each change in an iteration variable on each of the errors is included in the correction. The disadvantage in using the Jacobian matrix is the large number of derivatives needed, $(mn + n)^2$, and a simple means of obtaining these derivatives is needed. We have found that vector differentiation of the matrix equations given above does greatly simplify the derivation of the equations for calculation of the Jacobian.

By vector differentiation we mean the operation of differentiating one vector with respect to a second vector. The result is a matrix in which each column is the derivative of the first vector with respect to one of the elements of the second vector. For example $(\partial L/\partial V)$ is an n by n matrix in which the jth column is $(\partial L/\partial v_j)$, and the ij element is $(\partial l_i/\partial v_j)$.

$\underline{J}$ can now be defined by vector derivatives. First, however, it is partitioned into $(m+1)^2$ submatrices, each of size n by n. Subscripts are used to designate the submatrices. Thus, from the definition of the Jacobian matrix, we obtain

$$
\underline{J}_{ik} = \begin{cases} \dfrac{\partial E^i}{\partial V}; \, k = 1 & (14) \\[2em] \dfrac{\partial E^i}{\partial X^k}; \, 2 \le k \le m & (15) \\[2em] \dfrac{\partial E^i}{\partial T}; \, k = m+1 & (16) \end{cases}
$$

Before proceeding with the evaluation of Equations 14–16, some useful relations among the variables will be derived by differentiating the defining equations (Equations 1–3 and 6–10) with respect to the iteration variables. These results will be used when the error equations are differentiated implicitly.

From the overall material balance, Equation 1,

$$
\frac{\partial L}{\partial V} = -\underline{B}^{-1}\underline{A} = -\underline{R} \tag{17}
$$

Because $X^2 .. X^m$ are iteration variables,

$$
\frac{\partial X^j}{\partial X^k} = \underline{I}\,\delta_{jk}; \, 2 \le j, k \le m \tag{18}
$$

where $\delta_{jk} = 0$ if $j \ne k$ and equals 1.0 if $j = k$. From Equation 2 and the fact that X^1 is not an iteration variable,

$$
\frac{\partial X^1}{\partial X^j} = -\underline{I}; \, 2 \le j \le m \tag{19}
$$

Differentiating Equation 3 with respect to independent liquid compositions.

$$
\frac{\partial Y^j}{\partial X^k} = -\underline{V}^{-1}\underline{R}^{-1}\,\underline{L}\delta_{jk}; \, 2 \le j, k \le m \tag{20}
$$

$$
\frac{\partial Y^1}{\partial X^k} = \underline{V}^{-1}\underline{R}^{-1}\,\underline{L}; \, 2 \le k \le m \tag{21}
$$

For Y^1, a different result is obtained because of Equation 19.

To derive Equations 20 and 21, it must be remembered that the differentiation is with respect to X^k, holding V, T, and all other independent liquid compositions constant. With V constant, L must also be constant because of Equation 17.

Equation 3 will now be differentiated with respect to V, holding T and $X^2 .. X^m$ constant. In this case L is not constant, and differentiation of the first term BLX^j causes difficulty because L is a diagonal matrix and not a vector. This can be resolved by rewriting BLX^j as BX^jL, and now L is a vector. This special type of commutativity for the product of a diagonal matrix and a vector is used again in the product AVY^j and frequently in the derivations which follow. The derivative of Equation 3 by V gives,

$$\frac{\partial Y^j}{\partial V} = \underline{V}^{-1} \{\underline{R}^{-1}\, \underline{X}^j\, \underline{R} - \underline{Y}^j\}; \; 1 \leq j \leq m \tag{22}$$

Partial derivatives of the physical properties given by Equations 6–10 will also be needed in the derivations of the Jacobian submatrices. However, the exact form of Equations 6–10 is not known and will vary from problem to problem. The convention will be adopted that any partial derivative involving a physical property is to be interpreted using the variables given as arguments in Equations 6–10. For example, $(\partial G/\partial Y^2)$ means the partial derivative of G with respect to Y^2 holding $Y^3 \ldots Y^m$ and T constant. All vector derivatives of physical property vectors will be diagonal matrices. This is necessary because the physical properties in any one stage are functions only of the compositions and temperature in that stage.

The Jacobian Submatrices

Seven different equations are needed to calculate the various submatrices of $\underline{J}$:

1. The first group of submatrices is obtained by differentiating the error vector with respect to independent compositions. The general equation is

$$\frac{\partial E^j}{\partial X^k} = \underline{\Lambda}^j \frac{\partial Y^j}{\partial X^k} + \underline{Y}^j \sum_{p=2}^{m} \left(\frac{\partial \Lambda^j}{\partial Y^p}\right)\left(\frac{\partial Y^p}{\partial X^k}\right) - \underline{\Gamma}^j\underline{K}^j\left(\frac{\partial X^j}{\partial X^k}\right) - \underline{K}^j\underline{X}^j \frac{\partial \Gamma^j}{\partial X^k} \tag{23}$$

For $2 \leqslant j,k \leqslant m$, Equations 18 and 20 are used to obtain

$$\underline{J}_{jk} = -\underline{\Lambda}^{j}\underline{V}^{-1}\underline{R}^{-1}\underline{L}\delta_{jk} - \underline{Y}^{j}\left(\frac{\partial\Lambda^{j}}{\partial Y^{k}}\right)\underline{V}^{-1}\underline{R}^{-1}\underline{L} - \underline{\Gamma}^{j}\underline{K}^{j}\delta_{jk}$$

$$- \underline{K}^{j}\underline{X}^{j}\left(\frac{\partial\Gamma^{j}}{\partial X^{k}}\right); \ 2 \leq j,\,k \leq m$$

2. For $j = 1$ in Equation 23, Equations 19 and 21 are used

$$\underline{J}_{1k} = \underline{\Lambda}^{1}\underline{V}^{-1}\underline{R}^{-1}\underline{L} - \underline{Y}^{1}\left(\frac{\partial\Lambda^{1}}{\partial Y^{k}}\right)\underline{V}^{-1}\underline{R}^{-1}\underline{L} + \underline{\Gamma}^{1}\underline{K}^{1} -$$

$$\underline{K}^{1}\underline{X}^{1}\left(\frac{\partial\Gamma^{1}}{\partial X^{k}}\right); \ 2 \leq k \leq m \tag{24}$$

3. The derivatives of the material balance errors with respect to vapor flows are evaluated:

$$\frac{\partial E^{j}}{\partial V} = \underline{\Lambda}^{j}\left(\frac{\partial Y^{j}}{\partial V}\right) + \underline{Y}^{j}\sum_{p=2}^{m}\left(\frac{\partial\Lambda^{j}}{\partial Y^{p}}\right)\left(\frac{\partial Y^{p}}{\partial V}\right) \tag{25}$$

and then using Equation 22

$$\underline{J}_{j1} = \underline{\Lambda}^{j}\underline{V}^{-1}(\underline{R}^{-1}\underline{X}^{j}\underline{R} - \underline{Y}^{j}) + \underline{Y}^{j}\underline{V}^{-1}\sum_{p=2}^{m}\left(\frac{\partial\Lambda^{j}}{\partial Y^{p}}\right)\left(\underline{V}^{-1}\right)(\underline{R}^{-1}\underline{X}^{p}\underline{R} - \underline{Y}^{p})$$

$$1 \leq j \leq m \tag{26}$$

4. The energy balance errors are next differentiated with respect to vapor flows.

$$\frac{\partial E^{m+1}}{\partial V} = \underline{B}\,\underline{H}\,\frac{\partial L}{\partial V} + \underline{A}\,\underline{G} + \underline{A}\,\underline{V}\sum_{p=2}^{m}\left(\frac{\partial G}{\partial Y^{p}}\right)\left(\frac{\partial Y^{p}}{\partial V}\right) \tag{27}$$

Using Equations 17 and 22

$$\underline{J}_{m+1,1} = -\underline{B}\,\underline{H}\,\underline{R} + \underline{A}\,\underline{G} + \underline{A}\,\underline{V}\sum_{p=2}^{m}\left(\frac{\partial G}{\partial Y^{p}}\right)\underline{V}^{-1}(\underline{R}^{-1}\underline{X}^{p}\underline{R} \quad \underline{Y}^{p}) \tag{28}$$

5. The derivatives of the energy balances with respect to compositions are,

$$\frac{\partial E^{m+1}}{\partial X^{k}} = \underline{B}\,\underline{L}\left(\frac{\partial H}{\partial X^{k}}\right) + \underline{A}\,\underline{V}\sum_{p=2}^{m}\left(\frac{\partial G}{\partial Y^{p}}\right)\left(\frac{\partial Y^{p}}{\partial X^{k}}\right) \tag{29}$$

Then, using Equation 20, and after some rearrangement.

$$\underline{J}_{m+1,k} = \underline{B}\,\underline{L}\left(\frac{\partial H}{\partial X^k}\right) - \underline{A}\left(\frac{\partial G}{\partial Y^k}\right)\underline{R}^{-1}\,\underline{L} \qquad (30)$$

$$2 \leq k \leq m$$

6. The derivatives of the material balance errors with respect to T are next calculated.

$$\frac{\partial E^i}{\partial T} = \underline{J}_{j,m+1} = \underline{Y}^i\left(\frac{\partial \Lambda^i}{\partial T}\right) - \Gamma^i\underline{X}^i\left(\frac{\partial K^i}{\partial T}\right) - \underline{K}^i\underline{X}^i\left(\frac{\partial \Gamma^i}{\partial T}\right);$$

$$1 \leq j \leq m \qquad (31)$$

7. Finally, the derivative of the energy balance with respect to T gives,

$$\frac{\partial E^{m+1}}{\partial T} = \underline{J}_{m+1,m+1} = \underline{B}\,\underline{L}\left(\frac{\partial H}{\partial T}\right) + \underline{A}\,\underline{V}\left(\frac{\partial G}{\partial T}\right) \qquad (32)$$

Change of Iteration Variable

The Jacobian matrix developed above is based upon a specific model of a staged system in which the flow rates, the temperatures, and the phase compositions are all unknown and must be determined. A variation of this model which often occurs in practice requires that a solution be found in which one or more of the flows has a fixed value. It is relatively simple to modify the iteration procedure and the Jacobian matrix for the case of fixed vapor flows by substituting one of the elements of Q, the heat exchange vector, for each of the vapor flows which is to be fixed.

To interchange the variables v_i and q_j, the following procedure can be used. The Jacobian matrix is first modified by setting to zero the ith column of each of the submatrices J_{k1} for $k = 1$ to m. The ith column contains the effect of changing of v_i on each element of E; because q_j does not enter into any of the material balance equations, this column becomes zero. The ith column of $J_{m+1,1}$ is set equal to the jth column of an n by n identity matrix because q_j enters only the one energy balance equation. Upon solving for the correction vector $[(C)v_{+1} - (C)v]$ the ith element is now the correction for q_j. The correction to v_i is zero.

This procedure can only be used for fixed vapor flows. If liquid flows are to be fixed, a more complicated procedure is needed and will not be developed here. For simple countercurrent systems it is usually possible to fix product liquid flows by fixing certain vapor flows. An obvious modification of the above procedure can be used to fix temperatures if desired.

Initial Values for Iteration Variables

An important part of the iteration procedure is to select initial values for the iteration variables $(V, X^2 \ldots X^m, T)$. The correction sequence given by Equation 11 will converge for starting values sufficiently close to the solution. There is no simple way of knowing whether a given set of initial values is within this convergence range or not. Every effort should be made to make the initial values as good as possible. The method we have used is described here.

The temperatures of the reboiler and the condenser are first estimated using whatever information is available. The temperatures of the intermediate stages are then obtained by linear interpolation between condenser temperature and reboiler temperature.

The initial vapor flows are then calculated by estimating the liquid and vapor enthalpies and solving simultaneously Equation 1, the overall material balance, and Equation 4, the energy balance. The compositions are unknown for the enthalpy calculation. The procedure we have used is to set all compositions in all stages equal to $1/m$; this is a rough approximation.

After obtaining V and L, the activity coefficients and fugacity ratios are calculated using $1/m$ as the average composition in all stages. Then Equations 3 and 5 are simultaneously solved to give the liquid phase compositions. These compositions for each stage are then summed and normalized to one. These serve as the first estimates for $X^2, \ldots X^m$.

Modification of Correction Algorithm

The requirement that all of the variables lie within reasonable physical bounds can be incorporated into the correction algorithm. We have done this by specifying that at all times the vapor and liquid flows must be positive or zero; the phase compositions must not be negative or greater than one; and the temperatures must lie within predetermined limits. If at any time during the correction process these limits are exceeded, the current iteration is terminated. If it is the first iteration, then a new set of initial values will be needed. If it is the second or a later iteration, then it is assumed that the corrections made in the previous iteration were too large, and the current iteration is repeated using one-half the corrections predicted in the previous step. It may be necessary to repeat this process several times before all variables satisfy the given bounds. If during any iteration, more than 10 halvings of the correction are needed, we have terminated calculations and assumed the process was diverging.

Application to a Sample Problem

The results obtained in the solution of a sample problem are summarized here to illustrate the application of the method. An extractive distillation problem from Oliver (6) was used in which methylcyclohexane is separated from toluene by adding phenol. The column contains 11 stages (including the reboiler and condenser) and has a feed of 0.4 moles/unit time of methylcyclohexane and 0.6 moles/unit time of toluene to the fourth stage from the reboiler and 4.848 moles/unit time of phenol to the fourth stage from the condenser. We used the same physical property correlations as Oliver. The activity coefficients were obtained from a multicomponent form of the Van Laar Equation (7).

Table I.   Norms for Successive Iterations of Sample Problem

Iteration	Composition, ρ	Energy Balance, σ
1	2.9	2.8E4
2	1.6	1.6E4
3	1.5	7.2E4
4	1.4	3.2E4
5	1.2	9.8E3
6	5.8E-1	7.5E3
7	7.8E-2	1.5E3
8	1.7E-3	8.1
9	5.0E-6	2.0E-1

Results for successive iterations of a typical run are shown in Table I. The composition norm is defined as the Euclidean norm of the composition errors

$$\rho = \left(\sum_{i=1}^{n} \sum_{j=1}^{m} (e_{ij})^2 \right)^{\frac{1}{2}} \tag{33}$$

and the energy balance norm as

$$\sigma = \left(\sum_{i=1}^{n} (e_{i,m+1})^2 \right)^{\frac{1}{2}} \tag{34}$$

Values for these norms are given in Table I at each iteration. At iteration 9 the maximum error in any equilibrium equation is 2×10^{-6}, and the maximum energy balance error is 0.09 Btu/unit time.

The total time required for the nine iterations in Table I was about 4 min on an IBM 360/50 of which 1.5 min was execution time. The Jacobian was calculated for each iteration.

The results from some other runs are summarized in Table II. For each run the values of v_1 and v_{11} were held constant by making q_1 and

q_{11} iteration variables. All other heat duties, q_2–q_{10}, were set to zero. For each run it is necessary to estimate the reboiler and condenser temperatures to initiate calculations. The starting value method described previously was used to calculate all other starting values for the iteration variables. Values of v_{11} around 0.4 moles/unit time are interesting because v_{11} is the vapor product and should be mostly methylcyclohexane.

Discussion

The last two iterations in Table I clearly indicate quadratic convergence rates. This is especially evident in the composition norm where the error is roughly squaring in each iteration. The energy balance norm for the last iteration does not decrease as much as it should, but this undoubtedly results from round-off errors in the computer when using single precision arithmetic. The maximum energy balance error in iteration 9 is 0.09 Btu/unit time, and the enthalpies which are being summed in the energy balance equation are of the order of 50,000 Btu/ unit time. The fact that quadratic convergence is obtained is strong evidence that the Jacobian matrix has been correctly calculated and that the derived equations are correct. It is unlikely that the norms could decrease as they do in the last two iterations if the Jacobian were incorrect.

The first seven iterations in Table I show slow linear convergence. The correction-halving procedure outlined previously was used at least once in iterations 2–6. The other runs in Table II behaved similarly. All took more than nine iterations, and for each case the norms would decrease slowly (even occasionally rising for one iteration) until the last two or three iterations when they would dramatically decrease. Two of the runs did not converge.

The results in Table II indicate that for a reasonably wide range of vapor flows and starting conditions the correction method proposed

Table II.   Results for Different Vapor Flows and Starting Conditions for Sample Problems

Condenser		Reboiler		Number of
Temp. t_{11}	*Vapor Flow* v_{11}	*Temp.* t_1	*Vapor Flow* v_1	*Iterations to Converge*
210	.5	270	1.5	9 [a]
270	.8	330	1.5	10
210	.8	275	1.0	17
210	.1	275	1.5	Diverge
220	.4	300	1.0	10
210	.4	275	1.0	Diverge

[a] This is run reported in Table I.

here will give a good solution for this problem. The system studied should be a good test because it is highly nonideal. An indication of this is that temperature and composition maxima and minima were found for most problems when these variables were plotted against stage number.

Many variations of the correction method we have proposed can be used. Among these are the use of the same Jacobian for several iterations and the use of modified Newton methods such as Marquardt's method (8). We have tried Marquardt's method on some of these problems without observing any significant improvement, but this is only a tentative evaluation. Improved methods for generating starting conditions would be helpful.

A comparison of the method proposed in this paper with other methods is difficult because there are few published solutions for nonideal distillation problems. We were unable to find a completely solved problem with all material and energy balances satisfied. We have demonstrated that the Jacobian matrix gives rapid convergence in the vicinity of the solution, and this method might serve as a basis to evaluate other methods.

Acknowledgment

The authors wish to acknowledge the assistance of the Computer Center at the University of Pittsburgh.

List of Symbols

General: A lower case symbol is a scalar. An upper case symbol is a column vector. An upper case symbol with a superscript is a column vector formed by removing the column indicated by the superscript from the matrix with the same name. Underlined upper case symbols are matrices. If a symbol is defined as a vector then when underlined, it represents a diagonal matrix with the same elements as the vector. A matrix with a superscript is always a diagonal matrix.

$\underline{A}$ Vapor distribution matrix: $a_{ii} = -1$, $a_{ij} =$ fraction of total vapor leaving stage j which goes to stage i

$\underline{B}$ Liquid distribution matrix: $b_{ii} = -1$, $b_{ij} =$ fraction of total liquid leaving stage j which goes to stage i

C The direct sum of the independent variables, $(V, X^2, \ldots X^m, T)$

D The direct sum of the error vectors, $(E^1, \ldots E^{m+1})$

$\underline{E}$ Error matrix, the columns are defined by Equations 12 and 13

$\underline{F}$ Feed matrix: f_{ij} is total feed of component j to stage i, mass per unit time

G Vapor enthalpy vector; g_i is specific enthalpy of vapor in stage i, energy per unit mass

H Liquid enthalpy vector; h_i is specific enthalpy of liquid in stage i, energy per unit mass

$\underline{\mathbf{I}}$ The identity matrix

$\underline{\mathbf{J}}$ The Jacobian matrix; it is partitioned into $(m+1)^2$ submatrices, each of size n by n. $\underline{\mathbf{J}}_{kj}$ is the submatrix in row k and column j of the partitioned matrix.

L Liquid flow rate vector; l_i is total liquid leaving stage i, mass per unit time

m Number of components

n Number of equilibrium stages

Q Heat exchange vector; q_i is rate at which energy is added to stage i by heat exchange, energy per unit time

Q_f Feed enthalpy vector; $q_{f,i}$ is enthalpy of feed entering stage i, energy per unit time

$\underline{\mathbf{R}}$ Defined as $\underline{\mathbf{B}}^{-1}\underline{\mathbf{A}}$; $\underline{\mathbf{R}}^{-1} = \underline{\mathbf{A}}^{-1}\underline{\mathbf{B}}$

T Temperature vector; t_i is temperature in stage i

U A vector each element of which is 1.0

V Vapor flow rate vector; v_i is the total vapor leaving stage i, mass per unit time

$\underline{\mathbf{X}}$ Liquid composition matrix; x_{ij} is composition of component j in liquid in stage i

$\underline{\mathbf{Y}}$ Vapor composition matrix; y_{ij} is composition of component j in vapor in stage i

$\underline{\Gamma}$ Activity coefficient matrix for the liquid phase; the ij element is the activity coefficient for component j in stage i

δ_{kj} Equal to zero when $k \neq j$; equal to 1.0 when $k = j$

$\underline{\Lambda}$ Activity coefficient matrix for vapor phase; the ij element is activity coefficient for component j in stage i

ν Subscript used to indicate iteration number

ρ Euclidean norm of composition errors, Equation 33

σ Euclidean norm of energy balance errors, Equation 34

Literature Cited

1. Tierney, J. W., Bruno, J. A., "Equilibrium Stage Calculations," *AIChE J.* (1967) **13**, 556.
2. Tierney, J. W., Yanosik, J. L., "Simultaneous Flow and Temperature Corrections in the Equilibrium Stage Problem," *AIChE J.* (1969) **15**, 897.
3. Tierney, J. W., Yanosik, J. L., Bruno, J. A., "Solution of Equilibrium Stage Models for Solvent Extraction Processes," *Proceedings International Solvent Extraction Conference 1971*, pp. 1051–1061, Society of Chemical Industry, London, 1971.
4. Roche, E. C., "Rigorous Solution of Multicomponent, Multistage Liquid-Liquid Extraction Problems," *Brit. Chem. Eng.* (1969) **14**, 1393.
5. Nelson, P. A., "Countercurrent Equilibrium Stage Separation with Reaction," *AIChE J.* (1971) **17**, 1043.
6. Oliver, E. D., "Diffusional Separation Processes," pp. 189–197, Wiley, New York, 1966.
7. Drickamer, H. G., Brown, G. G., White, R. R., *Trans. AIChE J.* (1945) **41**, 555.
8. Marquardt, D. W., "An Algorithm for Least-Squares Estimation of Nonlinear Parameters," *J. Soc. Ind. Appl. Math.* (June 1963) **2**, 431.

RECEIVED December 10, 1971.

9

Isobaric Vapor–Liquid Equilibrium in the Acetic Acid–Acetone System

R. JOE BURKHEAD and J. THOMAS SCHRODT

University of Kentucky, Lexington, Ky. 40506

Isobaric vapor–liquid equilibrium data for the system acetic acid–acetone have been obtained at 760 and 500 mm Hg, using an Altsheler still. Acetic acid associates in the liquid and vapor phases, and this is accounted for in evaluating modified activity coefficients for the components. This system primarily shows small negative deviations of the coefficients with a maximum and a minimum appearing at high acetone mole fractions for both pressures. In evaluating the thermodynamic consistency of the data, the Herington test for isobaric data gave values of D − J of 5.4 and 7.6 at 760 and 500 mm Hg, respectively. The Redlich–Kister integral area method with an estimate of the heat of mixing term gave areas of 0.023 and 0.025 at 760 and 500 mm Hg, respectively.

Consistent vapor–liquid equilibrium data are necessary to design all types of rectification devices. However, many industrially important mixtures are nonideal, particularly in the liquid phase, and predicting their equilibrium properties from fundamental thermodynamics is not possible. Thus, the correlating of experimental x–y–t and x–y–P data has developed as an important branch of applied thermodynamics.

The nonidealities of equilibrium mixtures result from various combinations of molecular interactions; one such interaction that has been recently studied is molecular association. Molecules of fatty acids such as acetic acid typically form dimers and, to a lesser extent, trimers by hydrogen bonding in the vapor and liquid states. Failure of the equilibrium data of binary systems containing acetic acid to meet established criteria of consistency based upon the Gibbs–Duhem relation has been observed by Rius *et al.* (*1*), Campbell *et al.* (*2*), Herington (*3*), and

Marek (*4*). Here we try to obtain x–y–t data for the acetic acid–acetone system at 760 and 500 mm Hg and to show how considering acid dimerization improves the results for thermodynamic consistency tests.

Equilibrium Theory

The liquid phase activity coefficient of a component in a L–V mixture is usually given by

$$\gamma_i^{L} = \frac{P\, y_i}{P_{oi}\, x_i}\, \theta_i \tag{1}$$

where θ_i is the imperfection pressure correction factor and the absent vapor phase activity coefficient is taken as unity. In systems containing a dimerizing component Equation 1 will not give thermodynamically consistent γ_i's. Consider for such a component in a binary mixture, the respective modified vapor and liquid equilibrium expressions,

$$K = \frac{\eta_{d2}}{\eta^2_{m2}\, P} \tag{2}$$

and

$$k = \frac{\varepsilon_{d2}}{\varepsilon^2_{m2}} \tag{3}$$

where η and ϵ represent true mole fractions and the subscripts $m2$ and $d2$, the monomer and dimer, respectively.

For the pure component Equation 2 is written as

$$K_o = \frac{\eta_d}{\eta^2_m\, P_{o2}} \tag{4}$$

As in any two phase binary system, considering the monomer and dimer as the two components, $\eta_m + \eta_d = 1$ and $\epsilon_m + \epsilon_d = 1$, will allow Equation 4 and the pure component form of Equation 3 to be reduced to

$$\eta_m = \frac{\sqrt{1 + 4K_o\, P_{o2}} - 1}{2K_o\, P_{o2}} \tag{5}$$

and

$$\varepsilon_m = \frac{\sqrt{1 + 4k_o} - 1}{2k_o} \tag{6}$$

The activity coefficient for the monomer of the pure associating component is given by

$$\gamma_m = \frac{P_{o2}\,\eta_m\,\Theta_m}{P_m\,\varepsilon_m} \tag{7}$$

and in the presence of a nonassociating component by

$$\gamma_{m2} = \frac{P\,\eta_{m2}\,\Theta_{m2}}{P_m\,\varepsilon_{m2}} \tag{8}$$

Combining Equations 4, 5, 6, and 7 an expression for the hypothetical saturation vapor pressure of the pure monomer is obtained:

$$P_m = \frac{\Theta_m\,k_o}{\gamma_m\,K_o} \cdot \frac{\sqrt{1 + 4K_o\,P_{o2}} - 1}{\sqrt{1 + 4k_o} - 1} \tag{9}$$

The stoichiometric mole fractions of the associating component are given by

$$y_2 = \frac{\eta_{m2} + 2\eta_{d2}}{1 + \eta_{d2}} \tag{10}$$

and

$$x_2 = \frac{\varepsilon_{m2} + 2\varepsilon_{d2}}{1 + \varepsilon_{d2}} \tag{11}$$

These give with Equations 2 and 3, respectively,

$$\eta_{m2} = y_2\,\frac{\sqrt{1 + 4K\,P\,y_2\,(2-y_2)} - 1}{2K\,P\,y_2\,(2-y_2)} \tag{12}$$

and

$$\varepsilon_{m2} = x_2\,\frac{\sqrt{1 + 4k\,x_2\,(2-x_2)} - 1}{2k\,x_2\,(2-x_2)} \tag{13}$$

If Equations 9, 12, and 13 are substituted into Equation 8, a modified equilibrium relation containing vapor and liquid associations factors Z_2 and Γ_2 results:

$$Z_2\,\Theta_2\,y_2\,P = \Gamma_2\,\gamma_2\,x_2\,P_{o2} \tag{14}$$

where

$$Z_2 = \frac{1 + \sqrt{1 + 4K_o\ P_{o2}}}{1 + \sqrt{1 + 4K\ P\ y_2\ (2-y_2)}} \tag{15}$$

and

$$\Gamma_2 = \frac{1 + \sqrt{1 + 4k_o}}{1 + \sqrt{1 + 4k\ x_2\ (2-x_2)}} \tag{16}$$

For a nonassociating component, B, in the mixture, the true mole fractions are related to the stoichiometric mole fractions by

$$y_1 = \frac{\eta_1}{1 + \eta_{d2}} \tag{17}$$

and

$$x_1 = \frac{\varepsilon_1}{1 + \varepsilon_{d2}} \tag{18}$$

These are combined with Equations 2, 3, 10, and 11 to obtain equations for the true mole fractions of 1 in the vapor and liquid phases, respectively:

$$\eta_1 = y_1\ \frac{1 + 4K\ P(2-y_2) - \sqrt{1 + 4K\ P\ y_2\ (2-y_2)}}{2K\ P(2-y_2)^2} \tag{19}$$

and

$$\varepsilon_1 = x_1\ \frac{1 + 4k(2-x_2) - \sqrt{1 + 4k\ x_2\ (2-x_2)}}{2k(2-x_2)^2} \tag{20}$$

A modified equilibrium relation for component 1 is written in terms of Z_1 and Γ_1 correction factors for the association of A in the vapor and liquid phases, by combining Equations 8 (written for component 1), 19, and 20:

$$Z_1\ \Theta_1\ y_1\ P = \Gamma_1\ \gamma_1\ x_1\ P_{o1} \tag{21}$$

where

$$Z_1 = \frac{2\ (1 - y_2 + \sqrt{1 + 4K\ P\ y_2(2-y_2)})}{(2-y_2)\ (1 + \sqrt{1 + 4K\ P\ y_2(2-y_2)})} \tag{22}$$

and

$$\Gamma_1 = \frac{2\ (1-x_2 + \sqrt{1 + 4k\ x_2(2-x_2)})}{(2-x_2)\ (1 + \sqrt{1 + 4k\ x_2(2-x_2)})} \tag{23}$$

The preceding derivations are given in more detail by Marek and Standart (5) and are applied by Marek (4) to several binary systems. The terms θ_1 and θ_2 are evaluated from partial molal volume data or approximated from generalized correlations. According to Marek and Standart, the products $\Gamma_1\gamma_1$ and $\Gamma_2\gamma_2$ must satisfy all criteria of thermodynamic consistency, as should γ_1 and γ_2 for nonassociating systems.

To evaluate the activity coefficients, $\Gamma_i\gamma_i$, of a L–V system containing an associating component, the only other data needed are the modified vapor phase association constants, K_o and K. These are a function of temperature and pressure, and for K they are also a function of the non-associating component. Values of K are scarce; however, they may be approximated by extrapolating K_o data to temperatures below the normal boiling point of the associating component.

Modified Redlich–Kister Test

One method of evaluating the overall thermodynamic consistency of binary, isobaric L–V equilibrium data is based on the equation

$$\int_0^1 \ln \frac{\gamma_2}{\gamma_1}\ dx_1 = \int_{T_1}^{T_2} \frac{\Delta h^M}{RT^2}\ dT \tag{24}$$

The greater the heats of mixing and differences of boiling points of the components, the greater the value of the rhs integral. In systems where this is true, this quantity is evaluated to test overall consistency.

If x–y–t data are available at more than one pressure and if the assumption

$$\left[\frac{\partial \ln \gamma_1}{\partial P}\right]_{T,\ \text{all}\ x_1} = 0 \tag{25}$$

is valid, then $\Delta h^M/R$ is determined as a function of x_1 and of T by obtaining values of $x_i d\ \ln \gamma_i/d(1/T)$ over a range of P (6). These $\Delta h^M/R$ values and Equation 24 will test for consistency.

Experimental

An Altsheler still was used to obtain the x–y–t data at 760 and 500 mm Hg (*see* Reference 7 for a description of this still). A schematic diagram of our apparatus is given in Figure 1.

The pressure of the system was controlled to within ±0.5 mm Hg for each series by a Cartesian diver manostat connected to a positive air leak, a vacuum pump, and a surge volume of 12 liters. An absolute mercury-in-glass manometer with a 0.1 mm sliding vernier was used to measure the pressure. Temperatures were monitored *via* two copper-constantan thermocouples; one was located just above the liquid surface and the other just below it. Maximum differences of 0.4°C were detected, but an average of the two readings was reported to 0.2°C. Glacial acetic acid and acetone, both meeting ACS specifications, were used.

To begin a run, the still was charged with 500 ml of solution and allowed to boil for 3–4 hours; equilibrium was assured by a constant boiling temperature for at least one hour. For the series at 500 mm Hg, ice water was circulated through the condenser to minimize vapor losses. Samples were withdrawn at the system operating pressure, and their densities determined at 25 ± 0.1°C. The composition was analyzed by this method because of the large difference in densities of the two components; measurements accurate to ±0.2 mole % were recorded.

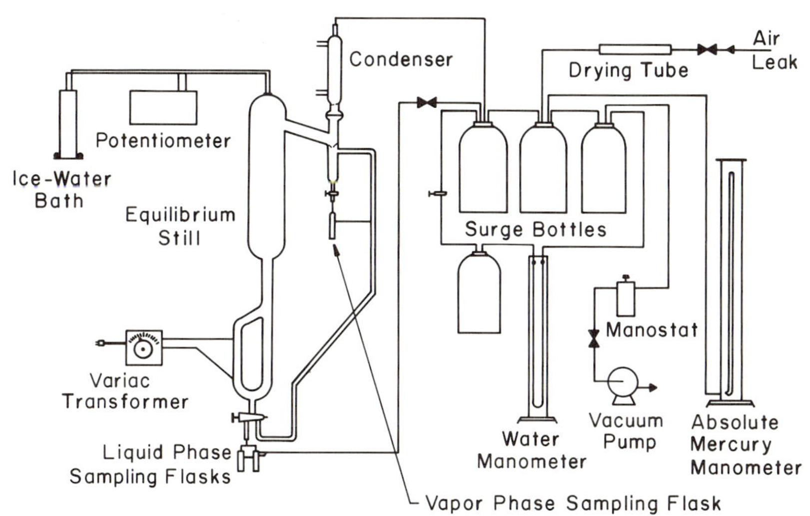

Figure 1.   Schematic diagram of experimental apparatus

Results and Discussion

The x–y–t data for the acetic acid–acetone system at 760 and 500 mm Hg are presented in Figure 2 along with the data of York and Holmes (8) at 760 mm Hg. Values of the standard activity coefficients, γ_1 for acetone

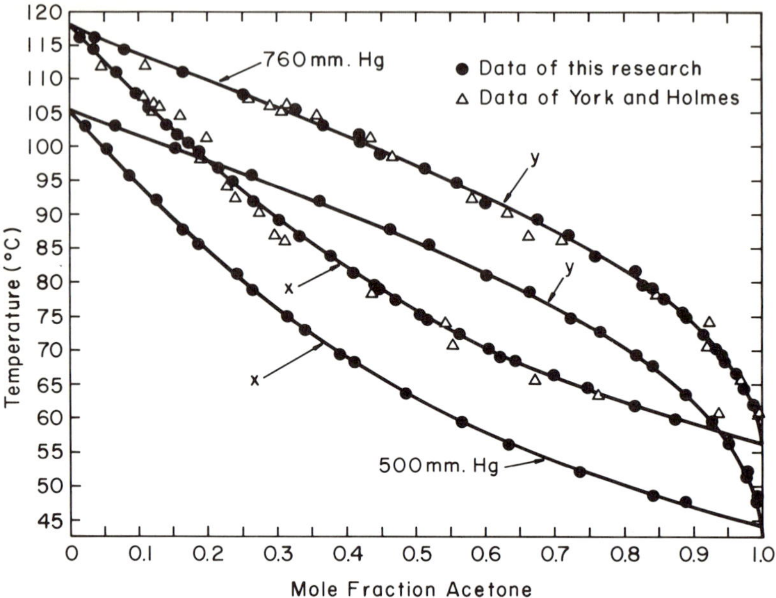

Figure 2.   Isobaric equilibrium data of acetic acid–acetone

and γ_2 for acetic acid, were calculated using: Equation 1, smoothed data from Figure 2, the Antoine vapor pressure equation for acetone (*9*), experimental vapor pressure data for acetic acid (*10, 11, 12*), and a table of imperfection pressure correction factors (*13*). These γ's are presented

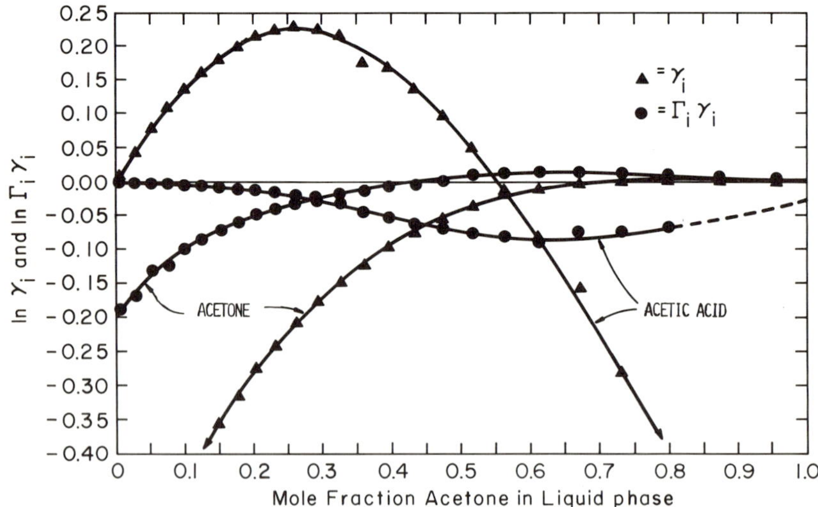

Figure 3.   Activity coefficients of acetic acid–acetone at 760 mm Hg

as a function of x_1 in Figures 3 and 4. Both sets of curves show positive and negative deviations from ideality and a maximum at $x_1 = 0.24$. Isobaric equilibrium studies by Rius *et al.* (*1*) of acetic acid and low molecular weight alcohol binary solutions resulted in similarly shaped curves. First, the data seem to be inconsistent since the maxima at $x_1 = 0.24$ are not balanced by minima at the same composition. Including the heat of mixing term that is necessary for isobaric data did not confirm consistency. To include the effect of the association of the acid, the modified activity coefficients, $\Gamma_1\gamma_1$ and $\Gamma_2\gamma_2$, were evaluated.

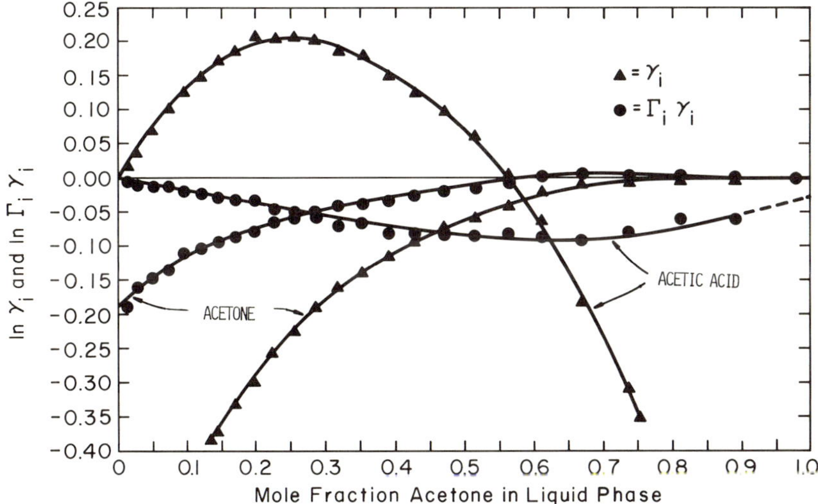

Figure 4.   Activity coefficients of acetic acid–acetone at 500 mm Hg

To calculate Z_2 and Z_1 appearing in Equations 14 and 21, from Equations 15 and 22, Marek's equation for K_o (*4*)

$$-\log K_{o(P \to o)} = 10.4205 - \frac{3166}{T} \tag{26}$$

and experimental values of K_o (*14, 15*) were plotted as a function of temperature and pressure. Differences between the values of $-\log K_{o(P \to o)}$ and the experimental values of $-\log K_o$ at the same temperature were then plotted as a function of temperature and pressure, and isobars through the points were extrapolated to the equilibrium temperatures. Addition of corresponding $\Delta \log K_o$ and $\log K_{o(P \to o)}$ from Equation 26 gave

$$-\log K_o = 1.4040 \log P_{o2} - 1.8821 \tag{27}$$

To determine K, the association constant of acetic acid in the mixture, the appropriate isobars, 760 and 500 mm Hg, were extrapolated to temperatures below the boiling point. The equations obtained for K were

$$-\log K_{(760)} = 9.9905 + 0.00224t - \frac{3166}{t + 273.2} \tag{28}$$

and

$$-\log K_{(500)} = 10.0505 + 0.00209t - \frac{3166}{t + 273.2} \tag{29}$$

The experimental data used to determine these constants were scant, and their quality is debated regarding their use for these determinations. Formulation of $\Delta \log K_o$ *vs.* T at constant pressure as a linear function is not necessarily correct and was done for lack of another method. Values of Z_2 and Z_1, calculated using Equations 15 and 23, were used in Equations 14 and 21 to evaluate $\Gamma_2\gamma_2$ and $\Gamma_1\gamma_1$.

Figures 3 and 4 also show the curves of *ln* $\Gamma_1\gamma_1$ and *ln* $\Gamma_2\gamma_2$ *vs.* x_1, and the appearance of these curves improve immediately by considering the association in calculating these modified activity coefficients. These plots show two unusual features—negative deviations in the activity coefficients and a maximum–minimum set at high mole fraction acetone.

Negative deviations showed by both sets of data—*i.e.*, values of $\Gamma\gamma$ less than one—are characteristic of electrolytes or of mixtures in which association or compound formation between the two components reduces

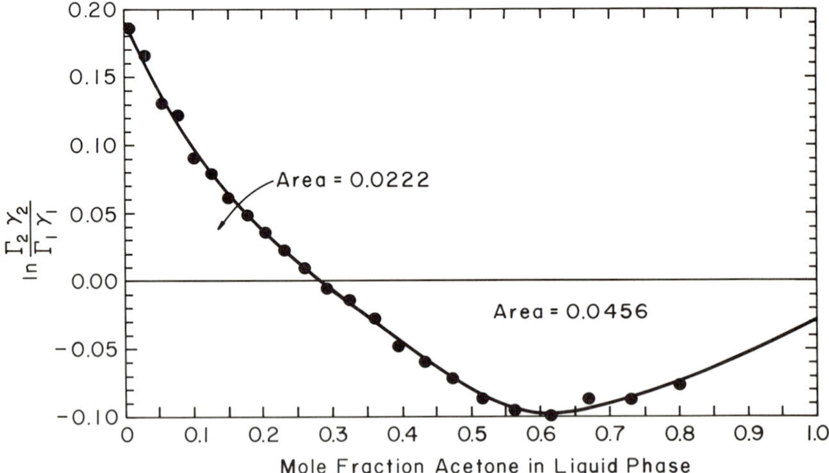

Figure 5.   Thermodynamic consistency plot for acetic acid–acetone system at 760 mm Hg

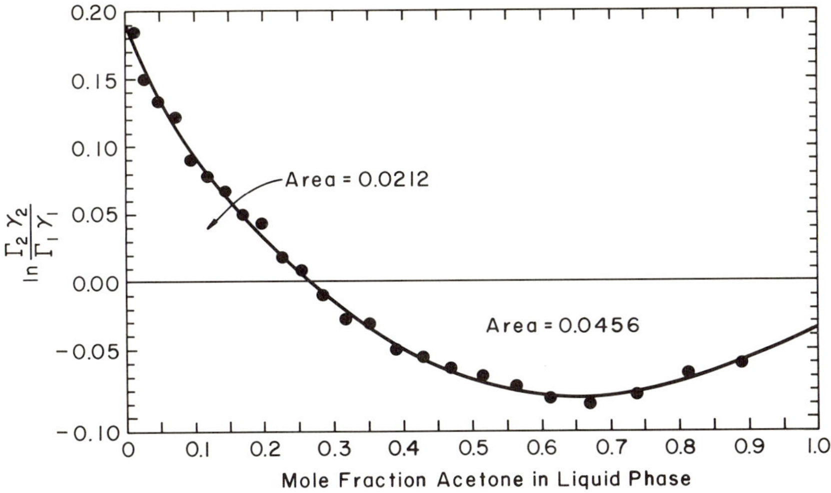

Figure 6.   Thermodynamic consistency plot for acetic acid–acetone system at 500 mm Hg

their volatility. Thus, it seems that there is association or attraction between the acetic acid and acetone molecules in the liquid, besides the acetic acid dimerization.

A maximum and minimum are observed in the curves of $\ln \Gamma_1\gamma_1$ and $\ln \Gamma_2\gamma_2$ for both sets of data. In both data sets these occur at x_1 about equal to 0.65. The values of $\Gamma\gamma$ are slightly greater at 760 mm Hg than at 500 mm Hg throughout the range of compositions. No other significant differences are noted between the two sets of curves.

From the plots of $\ln (\Gamma_2\gamma_2/\Gamma_1\gamma_1)$ *vs.* x_1, shown in Figures 5 and 6 for the two sets of data, values for the Herington test calculations were determined. According to Herington *(3)*, $D - J$ must be less than 10 if the data are consistent. At 760 mm Hg pressure, D is 33.6, and J is 28.2, giving $D - J = 5.4$. At 500 mm Hg pressure, $D = 36.4$ and $J = 28.8$, giving $D - J = 7.6$. Thus both sets of data seem to be thermodynamically consistent based on this test.

From Figures 5 and 6, the Redlich–Kister test apparently will not suffice for this system since the integrated areas of the curves are not zero. Retaining Equation 24, values of $\Delta h^M/RT^2$ were calculated using the procedure outlined above. The results are presented in Table I, along with values of

$$\int_0^1 \ln (\Gamma_2\,\gamma_2/\Gamma_1\,\gamma_1)\,dx_1,$$

Table I. Modified Redlich–Kister Consistency Test Results

P_T, mm Hg	$\displaystyle\int_0^1 \ln \frac{\Gamma_2\gamma_2}{\Gamma_1\gamma_1}\, dx_1$	$\displaystyle\int_{T@x_1=1}^{T@x_1=0} \frac{\Delta h^M}{RT^2}\, dT$	Δ Area
760	-0.0234	-0.0465	0.0231
500	-0.0244	-0.0492	0.0248

as determined from Figures 5 and 6. Although the differences between these values seem rather large, studying the procedures used in evaluating $ln\ (\Gamma_2\gamma_2/\Gamma_1\gamma_1)$ and $\Delta h^M/R$ indicates that the difference between these values is well within the limits of the experimental and procedural errors. One difficulty in evaluating these quantities is the relative smallness of the deviations for this system as compared with many other systems. Values of $ln\ \Gamma_1\gamma_1$ close to zero throughout the composition range cause slight errors in the system parameters to be significant in the area determinations. Primarily important for isobaric systems is the fact that the heat of mixing term in the equations derived from the basic Gibbs–Duhem relationship cannot be ignored and must be calculated to indicate the data consistency. Within the limits of experimental error, the modified Redlich–Kister test indicates marginal consistency of our data.

Acknowledgment

Grateful acknowledgment is made to the Ashland Oil and Refining Co. for supporting this work with a fellowship.

List of Symbols

D Herington test parameter
Δh^M heat of mixing
J Herington test parameter
K vapor phase association equilibrium constant
k liquid phase association equilibrium constant
P total pressure
R gas constant
T absolute temperature
t temperature
x stoichiometric liquid mole fractions
y stoichiometric vapor mole fractions
Z vapor phase association constant
Γ liquid phase association constant
γ activity coefficient
ϵ true mole fraction in liquid
η true mole fraction in vapor
θ imperfection pressure correction factor

Superscripts

L liquid phase
V vapor phase

Subscripts

d dimer
m monomer
o pure component
1 nonassociating component
2 associating component

Literature Cited

1. Rius, A., Otero, J. L., Macorron, A., *Chem. Eng. Sci.* (1959) **10**, 105.
2. Campbell, A. N., Kartzmark, E. M., Gieskes, J. M. T. M., *Can. J. Chem.* (1963) **41**, 407.
3. Herington, E. F. G., *J. Inst. Petrol.* (1951) **37**, 457.
4. Marek, J., *Collection Czech. Chem. Commun.* (1955) **20**, 1490.
5. Marek, J., Standart, G., *ibid.* (1954) **19**, 1074.
6. Null, H. R., "Phase Equilibrium in Process Design," McGraw–Hill, New York, 1970.
7. Altsheler, W. B., *Ind. Eng. Chem.* (1951) **43**, 2559.
8. York, R., Holmes, R., *Ind. Eng. Chem.* (1942) **34**, 345.
9. Lange, N. A., Ed., "Handbook of Chemistry," Rev. 10th ed., McGraw–Hill, New York, 1967.
10. MacDougall, J., Smith, H., *J. Amer. Chem. Soc.* (1936) **58**, 2585.
11. Ramsay, G., Young, R., *J. Chem. Soc.* (1886) **49**, 790.
12. Weast, R. C., Ed., "Handbook of Chemistry and Physics," 50th ed., The Chemical Rubber Company, Cleveland, 1970.
13. Burkhead, R. J., M.S. Thesis, University of Kentucky, Lexington, 1971.
14. Johnson, E. W., Nash, C. K., *J. Amer. Chem. Soc.* (1936) **58**, 2585.
15. Ritter, H. L., Simons, J. H., *J. Amer. Chem. Soc.* (1945) **67**, 757.

RECEIVED February 10, 1972.

10

Separation of Water, Methyl Ethyl Ketone, and Tetrahydrofuran Mixtures

HUGH M. LYBARGER and HOWARD L. GREENE

Department of Chemical Engineering, The University of Akron, Akron, Ohio 44304

Ternary vapor–liquid equilibrium data for the system water–methyl ethyl ketone–tetrahydrofuran were determined with a vapor recirculating equilibrium still of the type used by Hipkin and Myers. All experimental points were checked for thermodynamic consistency using the test proposed by McDermott and Ellis. Calculated liquid phase activity coefficients were correlated over the range of solvent concentrations using regression analysis. These results indicate a low boiling valley between the binary azeotropes of water–tetrahydrofuran and water–methyl ethyl ketone, but no ternary azeotrope was found. A solvent purification scheme, aided by development of a modified Thiele–Geddes computer program, was designed to separate the ternary mixture into pure components. The resulting system requires use of three ordinary distillation columns and extractive distillation, using dimethylformamide as the solvent.

Tetrahydrofuran (THF) and methyl ethyl ketone (MEK) are commonly used as solvents for high molecular weight polyvinyl chloride resins in topcoating and adhesive applications. Blends are used to combine the low cost of methyl ethyl ketone with the higher solvency and greater volatility of tetrahydrofuran. Because of the large amount of THF used, its relatively high cost, and air pollution considerations, recovery is normally necessary.

The solvent vapor may be recovered in commercially available activated carbon adsorption units. When the vapor–air mixture is passed through a bed of activated carbon, solvent vapors are adsorbed while the stripped air passes through. Periodic regeneration of the activated carbon with low pressure steam, however, generally contaminates the solvents with a large amount of water, increasing greatly the difficulty of subsequent separations.

This study was undertaken to obtain the necessary vapor–liquid equilibrium data and to determine the distillation requirements for recovering solvent for reuse from the solvent–water mixture obtained from adsorber regeneration. Previous binary vapor–liquid equilibrium data (2, 3) indicated two binary azeotropes (water–THF and water–MEK) and a two phase region (water–MEK). The ternary system was thus expected to be highly nonideal.

Results of this study have been used to design a solvent recovery system capable of separating each solvent into its original pure state. If separation of the THF–MEK mixture is unnecessary or if purity requirements are less demanding, the proposed system could be appropriately simplified.

Experimental

A vapor-recirculating equilibrium still similar to that described by Hipkin and Myers (1) was used to determine vapor–liquid equilibrium data for the system, water–MEK–THF. In this still shown schematically in Figure 1, a recirculating vapor is continuously contacted with a static liquid sample. The vapor–liquid system is enclosed by a jacket where

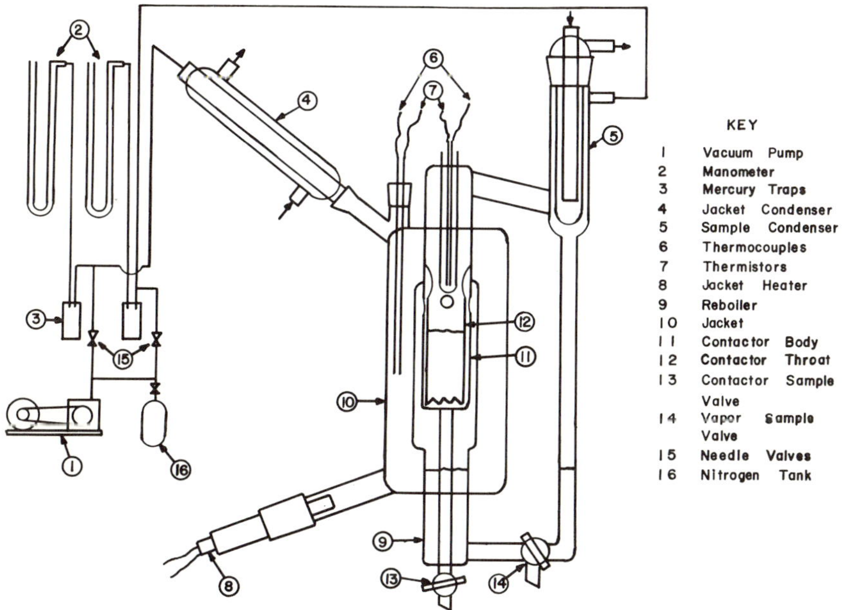

Figure 1.   Schematic diagram of the equilibrium still

Table I. Liquid Phase

Run No.	y_{water}, mole fr.	y_{MEK}, mole fr.	y_{THF}, mole fr.	x_{water}, mole fr.	x_{MEK}, mole fr.
1	.288	.181	.532	.561	.166
3	.217	.289	.494	.486	.237
4	.256	.177	.566	.866	.039
5	.257	.209	.534	.506	.181
6	.275	.388	.337	.377	.399
7	.236	.223	.541	.460	.211
8	.199	.102	.699	.322	.124
9 [a]	.226	.178	.596	.697	.092
10	.297	.478	.225	.375	.486
11	.244	.216	.540	.508	.194
12	.226	.058	.717	.585	.046
13	.234	.162	.604	.869	.037
14	.267	.327	.407	.379	.342
15	.314	.299	.387	.507	.267
16	.250	.182	.568	.507	.169
17	.247	.174	.580	.438	.181
18	.121	.039	.841	.071	.062
19	.103	.278	.619	.043	.409
20	.230	.619	.152	.110	.787
21	.163	.123	.714	.118	.197
22	.248	.477	.275	.184	.607
23	.311	.599	.090	.281	.665
24	.269	.291	.440	.438	.287
25	.244	.304	.452	.289	.374
26	.215	.040	.746	.296	.051
27	.181	.350	.474	.501	.279
28	.206	.284	.510	.169	.409
29 [a]	.262	.284	.453	.594	.208
				.862	.064
30	.165	.436	.399	.093	.587
31	.201	.149	.650	.189	.213
32	.095	.523	.383	.034	.678
33	.219	.006	.775	.596	.005
34	.134	.000	.866	.091	.000
35	.153	.000	.847	.121	.000
36	.221	.000	.779	.424	.000
37	.211	.000	.790	.661	.000
38	.160	.018	.822	.131	.029
39	.141	.031	.828	.093	.048
40	.144	.059	.796	.113	.092
41 [a]	.293	.366	.342	.502	.315
				.892	.064
42 [a]	.353	.370	.277	.469	.383
				.914	.058
43	.197	.071	.732	.177	.103
44 [a]	.318	.447	.235	.518	.368
				.862	.101

[a] Two-phase run.

Activity Coefficients

X_{THF} mole fr.	γ_{water}	γ_{MEK}	γ_{THF}	Temp., °C.
.273	2.021	1.722	1.946	64.7
.276	1.710	1.891	1.752	65.3
.094	1.343	8.008	6.582	61.6
.313	2.065	1.878	1.738	64.0
.224	2.497	1.379	1.362	67.9
.329	1.925	1.612	1.587	65.8
.553	2.577	1.352	1.306	63.5
.212	1.267	3.058	2.794	64.9
.140	2.608	1.353	1.421	68.8
.298	1.846	1.723	1.777	65.3
.369	1.598	2.045	2.005	63.6
.095	1.088	7.152	6.462	64.2
.279	2.463	1.375	1.343	67.4
.226	2.157	1.611	1.570	67.5
.324	1.876	1.661	1.706	65.5
.381	2.143	1.476	1.483	65.5
.867	7.289	1.057	1.022	62.9
.548	8.396	0.980	1.041	67.4
.103	5.933	0.962	1.182	72.2
.686	5.455	0.989	1.035	64.8
.209	4.274	1.050	1.136	69.6
.054	3.385	1.167	1.407	70.5
.275	2.188	1.481	1.492	67.0
.338	2.994	1.186	1.242	67.1
.653	3.101	1.318	1.204	62.9
.220	1.244	1.791	1.968	67.7
.422	4.588	1.060	1.173	65.7
.197				67.4
.074				
.321	5.872	1.020	1.099	68.8
.598	4.179	1.108	1.086	64.7
.288	8.089	0.966	1.086	71.5
.399	1.558	1.845	2.038	63.1
.909	6.745	0.000	1.052	61.4
.879	5.455	0.000	1.022	62.7
.577	2.321	0.000	1.465	62.0
.339	1.375	0.000	2.467	62.7
.840	5.186	1.054	1.025	63.1
.859	6.412	1.087	1.010	63.1
.796	5.343	1.065	1.036	63.5
.184				68.3
.044				
.149				68.8
.028				
.721	4.738	1.162	1.063	63.1
.113				70.3
.037				

hydrocarbon vapor is maintained at the boiling temperature of the liquid sample in the contactor. The still is thoroughly insulated so that the liquid and vapor in the contactor are maintained at adiabatic conditions.

Standardized procedures for obtaining equilibrium and for sampling the resultant vapor and liquid, as outlined by Lybarger (7), were followed. All vapor–liquid equilibrium data were obtained at a constant pressure of 730 mm of mercury which was achieved by applying vacuum or nitrogen pressure to the still (depending on atmospheric pressure) until the desired differential was obtained. After the vapor was recirculated, a constant pressure could be maintained in the still without further adjustments.

All liquid and vapor samples were analyzed on a Varian Aerograph Model 202-1B thermal conductivity gas chromatograph. A 12-foot column packed with Porapak Q, which gave a clean separation for water, was used, but it caused the peaks for methyl ethyl ketone and tetrahydrofuran to be slightly merged.

The chromatograph was calibrated using 11 solvent blends of known compositions. Area correction factors were determined from the standard samples, relating weight fraction to area fraction. All samples were analyzed twice, and the results were averaged. Calibration of the chromatograph with known water–MEK–THF samples indicated accurate determination to within ±0.002–0.005 mole fraction, depending on composition.

Results and Discussion

Vapor–Liquid Equilibrium Data. Forty-four pairs of vapor–liquid equilibrium data were determined for the ternary system; liquid compositions in the single and two-phase regions were studied. Results of these runs are summarized in Table I along with the liquid phase activity coefficients and boiling points obtained at a pressure of 730 mm of mercury. Tabulated compositions are averages of two analyses for each sample. Calculated liquid phase activity coefficients are based on Raoult's and Dalton's laws:

$$p_i = Py_i = \gamma_i \overset{*}{p}_i x_i \tag{1}$$

assuming vapor phase ideality.

The vapor–liquid equilibrium data for the single-phase runs are graphically shown in Figure 2 where the two-phase region at 60°C is also plotted to indicate the extent of partial miscibility at the boiling point. A line connects each pair of vapor–liquid equilibrium compositions.

Temperature results for the vapor–liquid equilibrium data indicate a low boiling valley connecting the binary azeotropes of water–MEK (66.2 mole % MEK, normal boiling point 73.4°C) and water–THF

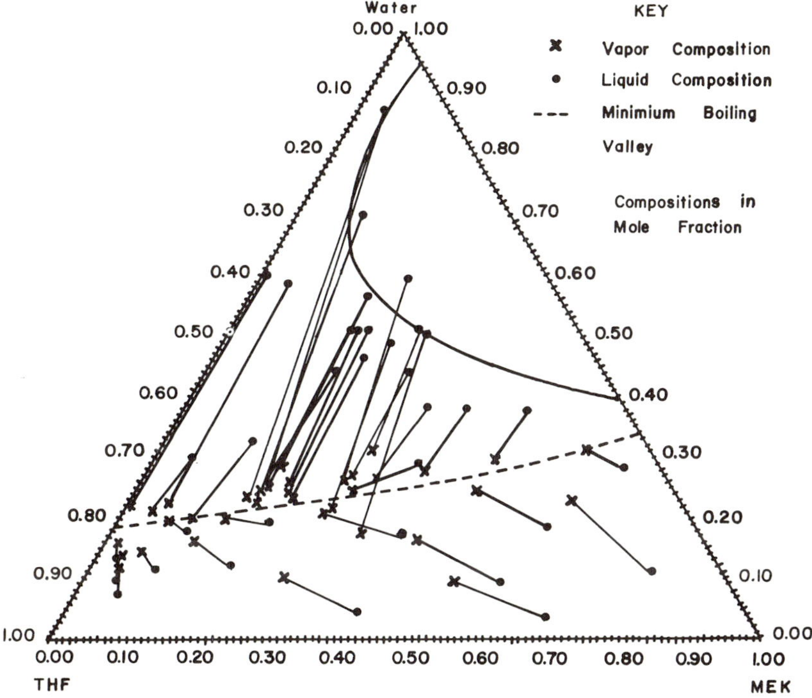

*Figure 2.   Ternary vapor–liquid equilibrium data for the one-phase region at
730 mm mercury absolute pressure with the solubility envelope for 60°C*

(81.7 mole % THF, normal boiling point 64.0°C). The dashed line
shown in Figure 2 indicates the approximate location of this valley.

Results for the two-phase runs are plotted in Figure 3 along with
the solubility envelope at 60°C. Although the equilibrium still was not
designed for two-phase operation, it was possible to obtain the necessary
data for this solvent system since the vapor in equilibrium with the two-
phase liquid was always single-phase when condensed. Several two-phase
samples were analyzed after cooling had occurred, accounting for the fact
that the ends of the liquid–liquid tielines in this region do not quite
extend to the solubility curve. Equilibrium vapor compositions corresponding to the liquid compositions are also plotted in Figure 3 and,
except for Run 42 which experienced severe bumping during boiling,
fall along an almost straight line.

For a ternary system the composition of vapor in equilibrium with
a heterogeneous liquid mixture can be related to the liquid compositions
by two relationships (5). First, the same vapor composition will result
from any liquid composition on a given liquid–liquid tieline. Second, a

smooth curve can be drawn through the vapor compositions in equilibrium with heterogeneous liquid compositions. This curve extends from the vapor in equilibrium with the binary heterogeneous azeotrope to vapor in equilibrium with the homogeneous liquid where the compositions of the two liquid phases become coincident (the plait point). With these two relationships, one can closely approximate the composition of vapor in equilibrium with a given two-phase liquid from Figure 3.

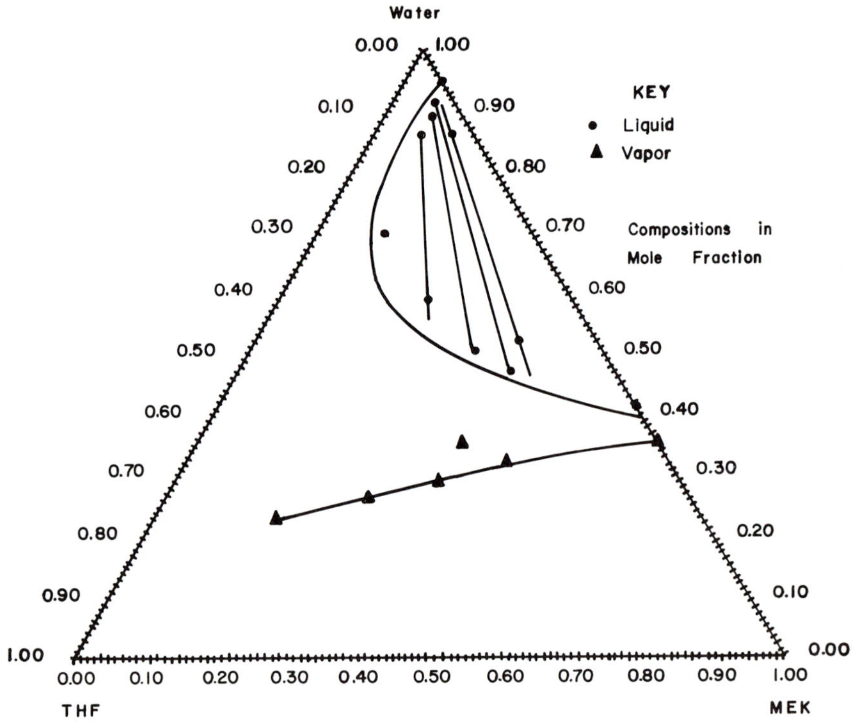

Figure 3. *Ternary vapor–liquid equilibrium data for the two-phase region at 730 mm mercury absolute pressure with the solubility envelope for 60°C*

Thermodynamic Consistency. The test developed by McDermott and Ellis (6) was used to determine the thermodynamic consistency of the vapor–liquid equilibrium data. This test involves calculation of the deviation, (D_{cd}), between pairs of points (c, d) as defined below:

$$D_{cd} = \sum_{i=1}^{n} (x_{ic} + x_{id})(\log \gamma_{id} - \log \gamma_{ic}) \qquad (2)$$

This deviation is derived from the isothermal–isobaric form of the Gibbs–Duhem equation and can be applied to isobaric equilibrium data by minimizing the composition and temperature differences between pairs of points. This was done by choosing data paths through the ternary equilibrium diagram so that differences in composition and temperature between pairs of points were minimized. A point was considered to be inconsistent if it deviated more than 0.02 with both of its neighbors. This deviation was chosen since it approached the approximate limit of the deviation caused by analytical inaccuracy. Runs 1, 4, 5, 13, 15, 23, 27, and 28 were determined to be inconsistent on this basis.

Correlation of Liquid Phase Activity Coefficients. For activity coefficients to be used in distillation calculations, they are normally represented as a function of composition. Here a multiple regression computer program was used to determine the coefficients for an equation of the form

$$ln\gamma_i = a_0 + a_1x_1 + a_2x_2 + a_3x_3 + a_4x_1^2 + a_5x_2^2 + \tag{3}$$
$$a_6x_3^2 + a_7x_1x_2 + a_8x_1x_3 + a_9x_2x_3$$

where x_1, x_2, and x_3 are the liquid mole fractions of water, methyl ethyl ketone, and tetrahydrofuran, respectively.

Terms were deleted from the regression equation until an equation containing only terms having a confidence level of greater than 80% to improve fit (in terms of sum of squares error) was obtained. Coefficients ($a_i's$) for the resulting simplified equations are summarized in Table II with an estimate of fit.

Table II. Regression Analysis Coefficients Used in Equation 3

	a_0	a_1 [a]	a_4	a_5
Water (1) (R=0.996)	2.2301	−4.5041	2.4778	—
MEK (2) (R=0.983)	−0.0426	—	2.0063	−0.1641
THF (3) (R−0.997)	−0.0017		2.0828	0.1995

[a] All a_i's not listed above were determined to be zero.

For mixtures containing more than 0.95 mole fraction of either water or MEK, respective activity coefficients for water or MEK are recommended to be chosen as 1.0 rather than the value predicted by the regression equations since insufficient data in these regions cause activity coefficients to deviate somewhat from the required terminal value of unity.

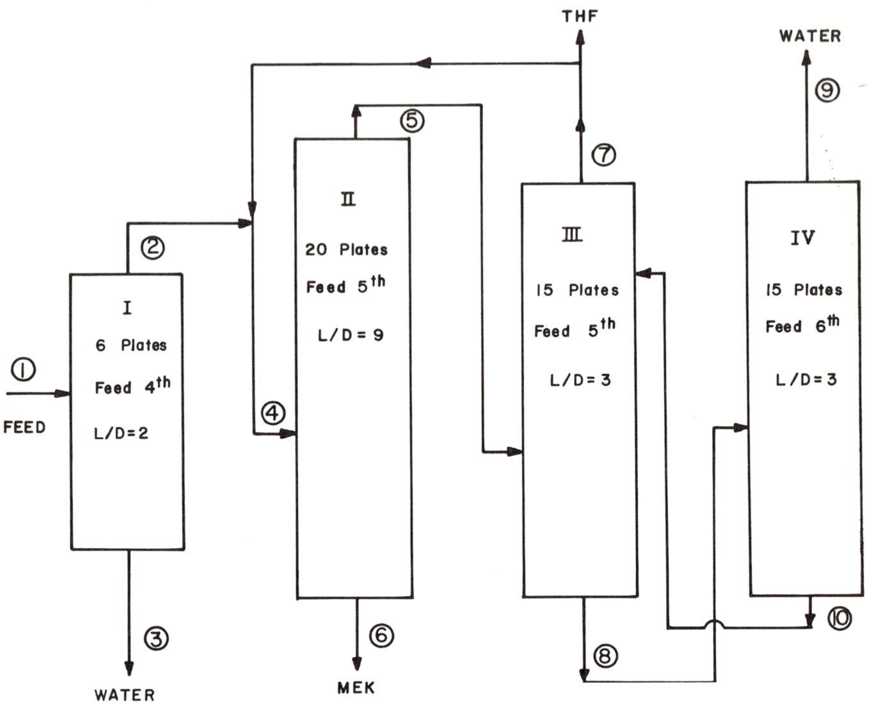

Figure 4.   Schematic diagram of solvent separation scheme

Ternary Separation By Distillation. To design a recovery system, a starting composition of 85 mole % water, 7.5 mole % tetrahydrofuran, and 7.5 mole % methyl ethyl ketone was chosen. This assumes 1.5 pounds of steam per pound of solvent are used for regeneration and a blend of equal amounts of the solvents for the polyvinyl chloride processing.

Figure 2 shows by the relative length of the connecting lines that in the region of water-rich liquid mixtures rectification to produce vapors rich in THF is easily obtained. However, the existence of a minimum boiling valley extending across the diagram from the THF–water binary azeotrope to the MEK–water binary azeotrope makes it impossible to remove all water from the overhead by a single distillation. The best that can be done in the initial distillation is an overhead product in the low boiling valley and a bottom product of substantially pure water.

Several alternatives exist to treat further the overhead stream. A second distillation, using the overhead from the initial distillation as feed, would yield an overhead close to the THF–water binary azeotrope and a bottom in the region of the MEK–water binary azeotrope. These two streams could then be dried by removing water physically—by molecular sieve or calcium chloride treatment, etc.—to yield relatively pure THF and MEK.

A second alternative, using only distillation methods, is considered here. This method, shown schematically in Figure 4, involves treatment of the overhead from the first column (composition in the low boiling valley) by adding to it sufficient dry THF to bring the new feed composition across the low boiling valley. Distillation of this new feed yields the THF–water azeotrope as overhead and a bottom consisting of dry MEK or an MEK–THF mixture. This THF–water azeotrope may then be dried by extractive distillation with dimethylformamide, as has been previously discussed (*4*). The bottom product, as an MEK–THF mixture, is easily purified by an additional distillation, but with regulation of feed composition in the previous column, this stream may be made to approach pure MEK, eliminating the need for this subsequent distillation. Finally, a small column used to separate the solvent, dimethylformamide (DMF), from the water is necessary to complete the separation scheme.

Multicomponent Computer Methods for Sizing Required Columns. A modified Thiele–Geddes method, programmed for an IBM 370-155, was used to perform the calculations needed to size each required column. Experimental activity coefficient data were used to allow for non-ideal liquid phase behavior while energy balances, using estimated enthalpy data, were used to correct for non-constant molal overflow. The Theta Method was used for convergence, and all plate efficiencies were assumed to be 100%. (*See* Reference 7 for additional calculational details and a program listing.)

Table III.   Column Specifications

Stream No.	1	2	3	4	5	6	7	8	9	10
Flow Rate (moles/hr)	100	20.0	80.0	34.3	26.8	7.5	21.6	15.2	5.2	10.0
Composition (mole fraction)										
THF	.075	.374	—	.635	.799	.016	.999	—	—	—
MEK	.075	.369	.002	.215	.011	.984	—	—	—	—
H_2O	.850	.258	.998	.150	.190	—	—	.660	.999	.001
DMF	—	—	—	—	—	—	—	.340	.001	.999

Column Specification and Flowsheet. A schematic diagram of the solvent separation scheme and the results of the computer analysis for each column are shown in Figure 4 and Table III, respectively. Feed plate locations are given with respect to the bottom of each column. Plate requirements for columns III and IV, which contain dimethylformamide, are based on an extension of a previous design analysis by Shah and Greene (4).

Literature Cited

1. "Recovery of THF du Pont Tetrahydrofuran," E. I. du Pont de Nemours and Co. (Inc.), Electrochemicals Department, Wilmington.
2. *Methyl Ethyl Ketone*, Shell Chemical Corporation, Technical Publication SC: 50-2, New York.
3. Shnitko, V. A., Kogan, V. B., "Liquid–Vapor Equilibrium in the Systems Tetrahydrofuran–Water and Tetrahydrofuran–Ethylene Glycol and a Method for Dehydration of Tetrahydrofuran," *J. Appl. Chem. USSR* **4** (6) 1236–1242.
4. Shah, C. S., Greene, H. L., "Vapor–Liquid Equilibrium for the Ternary System Tetrahydrofuran–Water–Dimethylformamide," *J. Chem. Eng. Data* **15** (3) 408–411.
5. Hala, E., Pick, J., Fried, V., Vilim, O., "Vapor–Liquid Equilibrium," pp. 107–109, Pergamon, 1967.
6. McDermott, C., Ellis, S. R. M., "A Multicomponent Consistency Test," *Chem. Eng. Sci.* (1965) **20**, 293–296.
7. Lybarger, H. M., "Ternary Vapor–Liquid Equilibrium Data Applied to the Separation of a Mixture of Water, Methyl Ethyl Ketone, and Tetrahydrofuran," Thesis, The University of Akron (March 1972).

RECEIVED February 14, 1972.

Prediction of Vapor Composition in Isobaric Vapor-Liquid Systems Containing Salts at Saturation

D. JAQUES and W. F. FURTER

Department of Applied Chemistry, Royal Melbourne Institute of Technology, Melbourne, Victoria, Australia, and Department of Chemical Engineering, Royal Military College of Canada, Kingston, Ontario, Canada

A method is described for calculating equilibrium vapor compositions from boiling point vs. liquid composition data in ternary systems composed of two liquid components and a salt added to saturation. The procedure is tested on the ethanol–water system containing each of a wide range of inorganic salts at saturation. The results suggest that good quality T–Π–x *data will yield* y *values of comparable accuracy.*

To obtain vapor–liquid equilibrium data for binary systems, it is now well established that under certain circumstances it can be more accurate and less time consuming to measure the boiling point, the total pressure, and the liquid composition and then use the Gibbs–Duhem relationship to predict vapor composition (1) rather than to measure it. The disadvantage is that there is no way of checking the thermodynamic consistency of the experimental data.

For systems composed of two liquids and a salt at saturation, this procedure is especially attractive because there are considerable experimental difficulties in obtaining accurate x–y–T–Π data and the process is more time consuming than in the absence of salts.

A procedure is presented which is based upon Barker's method (2) for calculating vapor compositions from the known temperature dependence of the vapor pressure of the pure constituents, with suitable modification for the presence of salt, and from the dependence of the boiling point of the mixture with composition of the equilibrium liquid phase.

Procedure

A computer program is used which minimizes $\Sigma(\Pi-\Pi_c)^2$ where the total pressure is given by:

$$\Pi_c = xp'_1\gamma_1 + (1-x)p'_2\gamma_2 \tag{1}$$

Using p'_1 and p'_2 instead of the saturation vapor pressures of the pure liquid components allows for the presence of salt. For salt-saturated systems it is proposed to base the activity coefficients on a standard state of each liquid component saturated with salt. The activity coefficients are related to the liquid composition by using the two-constant Wilson equation (3) except for systems which show a region of immiscibility when the three-constant form is necessary. One advantage of the Wilson equation over other semi-empirical approximations for integrating the Gibbs-Duhem equation is that it has a degree of built-in temperature dependence for the liquid-phase activity coefficients. The two-constant form gives:

$$ln\ \gamma_1 = -ln(1-A_{21}(1-x)) + (1-x)\left\{\frac{(1-x)A_{12}}{1-A_{12}x} - \frac{xA_{21}}{1-A_{21}(1-x)}\right\} \tag{2a}$$

$$ln\ \gamma_2 = -ln(1-A_{12}x) - x\left\{\frac{(1-x)A_{12}}{1-A_{12}x} - \frac{xA_{21}}{1-A_{21}(1-x)}\right\} \tag{2b}$$

When the best values of A_{21} and A_{12} have been found, the vapor composition is calculated:

$$ln(1-y) = ln((1-x)p'_2/\Pi) - (B_{22}-V_2)(\Pi-p'_2)/RT - ln(1-A_{12}x)$$
$$- x\left\{\frac{(1-x)A_{12}}{1-A_{12}x} - \frac{xA_{21}}{1-A_{21}(1-x)}\right\} \tag{3}$$

The term involving the mixed second virial coefficients was not used because of the uncertainties in the values of the second virial coefficients of the pure components.

Application

The method described above is applied to the ethanol–water system which has been saturated in turn with each of a wide range of inorganic salts. The vapor pressure of water saturated with salts over a temperature range is available for many salts (4). For ethanol these data are unavailable, and a correction to the saturation vapor pressure is applied by multiplying by the ratio of the vapor pressure of ethanol saturated with salt to the vapor pressure of pure ethanol at the salt solution boiling point. This ratio, ϵ, is assumed to be independent of temperature. Interpolating literature data yielded the required values of the molar volumes of the two liquids (5) at the appropriate temperatures and the second virial coefficients of water (6) and ethanol (7). An example of the fit is shown in Table I.

Table I.   Calculated Vapor Compositions from Fit of Isobaric Data Ethanol–Water–Saturated Ammonium Chloride (14)

x	y	T	T–x fit $(y-y_c)$	G^E/RT–x fit $(y-y_c)$
.034	.495	93.8	.000	.003
.074	.595	87.2	$-.012$	$-.007$
.124	.646	84.2	$-.007$	.000
.170	.674	82.5	$-.005$	.004
.284	.696	81.7	$-.001$	.009
.446	.720	80.8	$-.003$	.005
.633	.752	79.4	$-.019$	$-.016$
.759	.807	78.5	$-.012$	$-.014$
.858	.869	77.7	$-.006$	$-.011$
.938	.936	77.9	.001	$-.003$
Sample deviation			.0098	.0098

As an alternative, these data were also fitted to Wilson's free energy equation:

$$G^E/RT = -x \, ln(1-A_{21}(1-x)) - (1-x) \, ln(1-A_{12}x) \qquad (4)$$

and the vapor composition was again calculated by using Equation 3. A direct comparison can be made by examining the sample deviation of the vapor composition from both fittings. Table II presents the two sets of sample deviations based upon vapor compositions. The values of σ_Π and $\sigma_{G^E/RT}$ indicate that some of the data are of dubious accuracy—*i.e.*, low consistency and/or high experimental scatter. Graphical smoothing of the observed T–*x* data would have reduced the values of the sample deviations by removing the experimental scatter component, but it was considered desirable to use the raw data.

The validity of the T–*x* estimation for the ethanol–water binary without salt was checked using three sets of literature data. The results are included in Table II, and Otsuki's data (8) are shown in Figure 1. Calculated and experimental *y*-values agree satisfactorily.

Addition of a salt in many cases results in a considerably wider boiling range, and this would affect the heat of mixing term and lead to a poorer fit of the data. However, this is unlikely to be an important factor because it has been shown (9) that a good fit is obtained with isobaric data for the methanol–anisole system which has a 64°C boiling range. Comparing the two sets of results in Table II indicates that the $G^E/RT–x$ fit is generally superior, but for the better data as indicated by small sample deviations of pressure and free energy, the differences are small. This conclusion is not unexpected. However, if the following equation

$$ln\ y = ln(xp'_1/\Pi) - (B_{11}-V_1)(\Pi-p'_1)/RT - ln(1-A_{21}(1-x))$$
$$+ (1-x) \left\{ \frac{(1-x)\ A_{12}}{1-A_{12}x} - \frac{xA_{21}}{1-A_{21}\ (1-x)} \right\}$$

(5)

is used to calculate the vapor composition instead of Equation 3, in every case except for barium nitrate the opposite is true. This effect is not marginal, and an explanation is offered below.

Table II. Comparison of the T–x Fit and the $G^E/RT–x$ Fit Using the Wilson Equation

Salt	$\sigma\Pi$	σy	$\sigma G^E RT$	$\sigma' y$	Reference
—	4.88	.0079	6.45	.0082	8
—	6.24	.0068	4.48	.0064	12
—	9.69	.0045	6.34	.0059	13
NH_4Cl	13.66	.0098	5.84	.0098	14
† NaCl	18.82	.0119	11.79	.0054	14
† NaBr	27.42	.0471	60.27	.0375	15
† $NaNO_3$	30.06	.0260	31.75	.0187	14
† KCl	31.40	.0301	28.74	.0200	14
KBr	28.09	.0109	10.72	.0150	15
KI	19.48	.0234	14.08	.0098	15
K_2SO_4	3.95	.0118	6.23	.0082	14
$Ca(NO_3)_2$	33.69	.0078	28.12	.0096	11
$Ba(NO_3)_2$	20.20	.0152	15.45	.0130	14
CuCl	10.31	.0092	7.54	.0096	14
$HgCl_2$	5.10	.0138	3.55	.0119	14
$HgBr_2$	8.40	.0273	17.47	.0261	14
HgI_2	13.69	.0142	13.98	.0146	14
$LiCl^a$	6.07	.0062	12.54	.0056	16
† $NaCl^b$	20.96	.0184	14.64	.0143	17
† $Na_2SO_4^b$	23.95	.0264	19.63	.0132	18
† KCl^b	22.90	.0180	10.14	.0088	17
KI^c	3.65	.0058	4.00	.0045	16
$BaCl_2^d$	11.42	.0110	4.34	.0085	11
KNO_3^e	4.94	.0099	7.70	.0078	19
$(NH_4)_2SO_4^e$	24.9	.0358	35.3	.0320	14

[a] Data of limited range: x = 0.3–1.0.
[b] Data of limited range: x = 0–0.8.
[c] Data of limited range: x = 0.2–1.0.
[d] Data of limited range: x = 0–0.6.
[e] Partially miscible systems–use of three constant Wilson equation.
† *See* text.

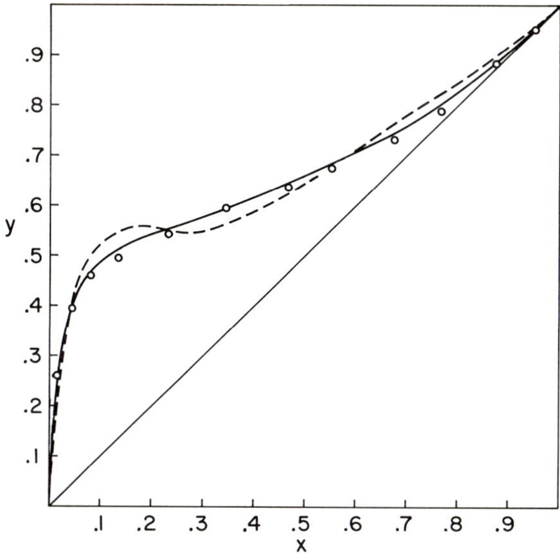

Figure 1. Comparison of the experimentally determined vapor compositions for the ethanol-water
system (8) with two constant Wilson T–x fit

Observed   ○

Calculated   ————————

An interesting anomaly occurred for the seven systems marked with
a dagger in Table II. The original computer program which was based
upon first order linearization of the normal equations failed to find a
solution for the G^E/RT–x fit for these systems. A second program used
a more powerful technique which used a new approach to variable
metric algorithms (10). Because the two constants in the Wilson equation cannot be greater than unity, a constraint is placed upon the plane
where a solution is sought. To free the program from this constraint,
A_{21} was replaced by $1-A^2$ and A_{12} by $1-B^2$. This program found a solution, but it did not represent a true minimum. The solution occurred at
a wall—*i.e.*, where $A_{21} = 1$, and analysis showed that this was the
lowest point of the A_{21}–A_{12} plane. Analyzing the remaining systems of
Table II showed that a genuine minimum—*i.e.*, a least value where the
first derivatives of the object function vanish—was found in all of these
cases.

The two systems containing potassium nitrate and ammonium sulfate each have a region of partial miscibility. Adding a third constant to
the Wilson equation allows correlation of such systems. The results are
shown in Table II and Figure 2. (The broken line of Figure 2 is a feature
of systems which show material instability. A graph of molar free energy

of mixing as a function of liquid mole fraction shows a convex upwards portion where a region of partial miscibility exists (*20*). The vapor–liquid equilibrium curve should, of course, be horizontal in the region of two liquid phases, but the form of the equation must give a continuous curve and hence cannot predict a horizontal line, which would amount to a region of discontinuity in the equation.)

The two-constant Wilson equation was chosen as the correlating equation rather than the three-constant Redlich–Kister equation (*21*) for two reasons. In a majority of the systems the sample deviation of vapor composition was smaller, and in certain cases the Redlich–Kister equation erroneously predicted phase separation. Figure 3 shows such an example.

Table III gives a complete listing of m, c, ϵ, A_{21}, A_{12}, and C values which allow us to estimate the vapor compositions of ethanol–water mixtures containing a wide range of inorganic salts.

Discussion

Different object functions (Π, y, $ln\ \gamma_2/\gamma_1$, etc.) have been used for many years; when discrepancies have arisen, at least one author (*22*)

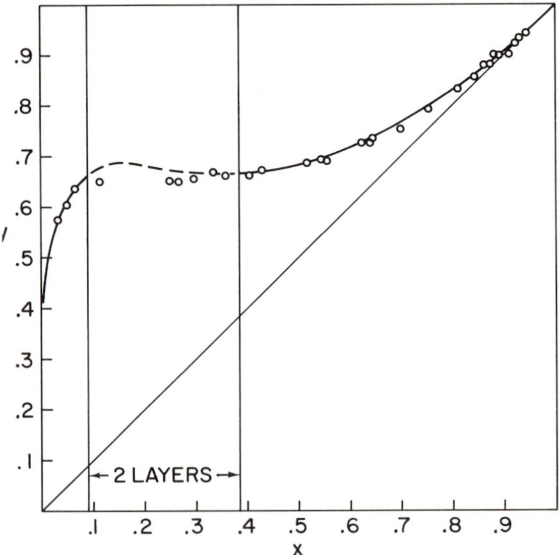

Figure 2.   Comparison of the experimentally determined vapor compositions for the ethanol-water-saturated potassium nitrate system (19) with the three constant Wilson T–x fit

Observed   O

Calculated   ————————

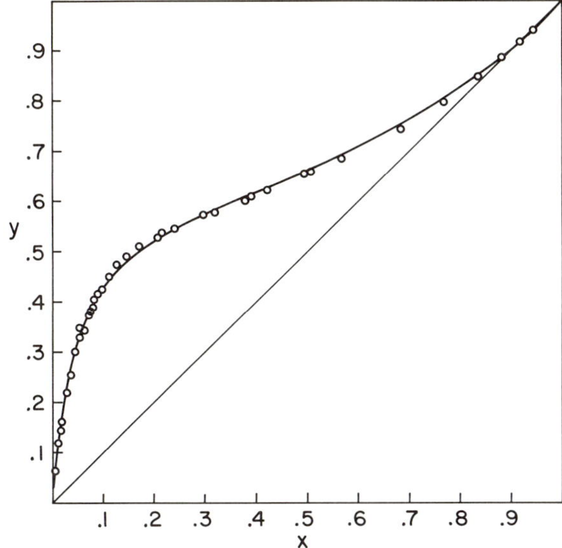

*Figure 3. Comparison of experimentally deter-
mined vapor compositions for the ethanol-water–
saturated potassium sulfate system (14) with (a)
two constant Wilson T–x fit and (b) three constant
Redlich–Kister T–x fit*

Observed   O

Calculated   (a) ——————— (b) — — — —

has attributed them to errors in data. Actually, there are three possible
sources of error:

1. The Wilson equation is an imperfect model. In the isobaric case
the effect of neglecting the temperature dependence of A_{21} and A_{12} and
in using the Gibbs–Duhem equation, which was derived for constant
temperature and pressure, add to the inherent imperfection.

2. All the experimental data are subject to error, and in the salt
effect field an adequate estimation of experimental errors is rarely made.
For example, without doing a statistical treatment of the error in the
measuring of temperature, a simple estimation of random experimental
error based upon the graphical smoothing of boiling point–composition
data for eight systems containing water, methanol or ethanol, and an
acetate salt at saturation [taken from the literature (23)] suggested an
overall average error of ±0.9°C on the boiling points.

3. The whole procedure, with or without salts, may not be based
upon sound statistical principles. Rather than using various object functions, it appears better to use a reliable statistical technique such as the
method of maximum likelihood (24) or the Bayesian approach (25),
both of which take into account the errors in all experimental observations in a logically justifiable fashion. The various discrepancies and
anomalies noted in the present work would be moderated by using either

Table III.   Constants for the T–x Fit Using the Wilson Equation

Salt	m	const.	ε	A_{21}	A_{12}	C	Reference
—	—	—	—	.8140	.1325	—	8
—	—	—	—	.7899	.1813	—	12
—	—	—	—	.8526	.0848	—	13
NH_4Cl	.9294	−.0032	1.013	.8829	.4154	—	14
NaCl	.9935	.1109	1.019	.9476	.3692	—	14
NaBr	.9174	.0776	0.912	.9138	.5005	—	15
$NaNO_3$	.8853	−.0704	1.020	.9420	.5592	—	14
KCl	.9547	−.0037	1.000	.9198	.4314	—	14
KBr	.9572	.0360	0.983	.9214	.2744	—	15
KI	.9383	.0719	0.886	.8433	.4000	—	15
K_2SO_4	.9962	.0105	1.023	.9188	.0802	—	14
$Ca(NO_3)_2$	1.0712	.9368	0.747	.8531	.0090	—	11
$Ba(NO_3)_2$	1	0	1.027	.8208	.1780	—	11
CuCl	1	0	1.042	.8486	.0565	—	14
$HgCl_2$	1	0	.892	.8314	.0791	—	14
$HgBr_2$	1	0	.965	.8428	.1263	—	14
HgI_2	1	0	1.010	.8267	.1095	—	14
LiCl	.9659	.9199	.492	.7926	.5457	—	16
NaCl	.9935	.1109	1.019	.9332	.3308	—	17
Na_2SO_4	1.019	.0969	1.000	.9349	.1633	—	18
KCl	.9640	.0235	1.000	.9307	.3226	—	17
KI	.9383	.0719	.975	.9275	.3285	—	16
$BaCl_2$	.9906	.0348	1	.9170	.2142	—	11
KNO_3	.8570	−.2250	1.000	.7515	−.3908	2.959	19
$(NH_4)_2SO_4$	.9731	.0487	1.011	.9409	.0449	1.250	14

estimate with the only sources of error being in the observations and in the phenomenological model.

Conclusions

A method has been developed for calculating equilibrium vapor compositions, based on boiling point *vs.* liquid composition data, for systems saturated with a salt. Such ternary systems in effect have been treated as binaries (26) in which the standard state of each of the two liquid components is that of being saturated with salt instead of being pure and with the pure-component vapor pressures being so adjusted. For example, in the ethanol–water–salt ternary systems tested, they have been considered as binaries composed of water saturated with salt as one component and ethanol saturated with salt as the other component. In the testing to which it has been subjected so far, the method seems encouraging.

Acknowledgment

The research for this paper was supported by the Defence Research Board of Canada, Grant number 9530-40. The authors are grateful to F. M. Larkin of the Computer Centre at Queen's University, Kingston, for many helpful discussions.

List of Symbols

Subscripts:

$\quad$ 1 = ethanol
$\quad$ 2 = water
$\quad$ c = calculated value

A_{21}, A_{12}, C	= empirical constants in Wilson equation
A,B	= empirical constants for use with Fletcher's subroutine
B_{ii}	= second virial coefficient of component i
G^E	= excess free energy of mixing
ln	= natural logarithm
log	= logarithm to the base 10
m, const.	= empirical constants in the equation:
	$\log p'_2 = m \log p°_2 - \text{const.}$
p'_i	= vapor pressure of component i saturated with salt
R	= gas constant
T	= absolute temperature
V_i	= molar volume of component i
x	= mole fraction of ethanol in the liquid phase, calculated on a salt-free basis
y	= mole fraction of ethanol in the vapor phase
γ_i	= activity coefficient of component i
ϵ	= ratio of vapor pressure of ethanol saturated with salt to the vapor pressure of pure ethanol at the salt solution boiling point
Π	= total pressure
$\sigma_{G^E/RT}$	= sample deviation of the excess free energy in Equation 4
σ'_y	= sample deviation of the vapor composition corresponding to Equation 4
σ_Π	= sample deviation of the total pressure in Equation 1
σ_y	= sample deviation of the vapor composition corresponding to Equation 1

Literature Cited

1. MacKay, D., Salvador, R. J., *Ind. Eng. Chem. Fundamentals* (1971) **10**, 167.
2. Barker, J. A., *Australian J. Chem.* (1953) **6**, 207.
3. Wilson, G. M., *J. Amer. Chem. Soc.* (1964) **86**, 127.
4. International Critical Tables, pp. 362–374, Vol. III, McGraw-Hill, New York, 1929.
5. Prausnitz, J. M., Eckert, C. A., Orye, R. V., O'Connell, J. P., "Computer Calculations for Multicomponent Vapor-Liquid Equilibrium," Appendix B, Prentice-Hall, 1967.

6. Rowlinson, J. S., *Trans. Faraday Soc.* (1949) **45**, 974.
7. Lambert, J. D., *Discussions Faraday Soc.* (1953) **15**, 226.
8. Otsuki, H., Williams, F. C., *Chem. Eng. Progr. Symp. Ser. 6* (1953) **49**, 55.
9. Cukor, P. M., Prausnitz, J. M., *Intern. Symp. Distillation, Inst. Chem. Engrs. (London)*, Section 3B, p. 73 (1969).
10. Fletcher, R., *U.K. At. Energy Authority Rept. TP383* (1969).
11. Rius Miró, A., Alvarez Gonzalez, J. R., Uriante Hulda, A., *Anales Real. Soc. Espan. Fis. Quim. (Madrid)* (1960) **56B**, 629.
12. Rieder, R. M., Thompson, A. R., *Ind. Eng. Chem.* (1949) **41**, 2905.
13. Furter, W. F., Ph.D. Thesis, University of Toronto, 1958.
14. Johnson, A. I., Furter, W. F., *Can. J. Chem. Eng.* (1960) **38**, 78.
15. Meranda, D., Furter, W. F., *A.I.Ch.E. Journal* (1972) **17**, 38.
16. Rius Miró, A., Otero de la Gandara, J. L., Alvarez Gonzalez, J. R., *Anales Real. Soc. Espan. Fis. Quim. (Madrid)* (1957) **53B**, 185.
17. idem., ibid. (1957 **53B**, 171.
18. Tursi, R. R., Thompson, A. R., *Chem. Eng. Progr.* (1951) **47**, 304.
19. Rieder, R. M., Thompson, A. R., *Ind. Eng. Chem.* (1950) **42**, 379.
20. Rowlinson, J. S., "Liquids and Liquid Mixtures," p. 144, 2nd ed., Butterworth, 1969.
21. Redlich, O., Kister, A. T., *Ind. Eng. Chem.* (1948) **40**, 345.
22. Newton, A., *Intern. Symp. Distillation, Inst. Chem. Engrs. (London)*, Section 3B, p. 82 (1969).
23. Meranda, D., Furter, W. F., *A.I.Ch.E. J.* (1971) **17**, 38.
24. Kendall, M. G., Stuart, A., "The Advanced Theory of Statistics," Vol. II, 2nd ed., Griffin, London, 1967.
25. Lindley, D. V., "Introduction to Probability and Statistics from a Bayesian Viewpoint," Cambridge, 1965.
26. Jaques, D., Furter, W. F., *A.I.Ch.E. J.* (1972) **18**, 343.

RECEIVED January 11, 1972.

INDEX